D1034773

West Hills College Coalinga
Fitch Library
300 Cherry Lane
Coalinga, CA 93210

DISCARD

DISCARD

■ INTRODUCTION TO STEREOCHEMISTRY

THE ORGANIC CHEMISTRY
MONOGRAPH SERIES

Ronald Breslow, EDITOR

Columbia University

EDITORIAL ADVISORY BOARD: **P. D. Bartlett,** *Harvard University*
David Curtin, *University of Illinois*
W. S. Johnson, *Stanford University*
J. D. Roberts, *California Institute of Technology*
R. B. Woodward, *Harvard University*

ORGANIC REACTION MECHANISMS

Ronald Breslow

Columbia University

MODERN SYNTHETIC REACTIONS

Herbert House

Massachusetts Institute of Technology

INTRODUCTION TO STEREOCHEMISTRY

Kurt Mislow

Princeton University

547.1223

INTRODUCTION TO STEREOCHEMISTRY

KURT MISLOW PRINCETON UNIVERSITY

W. A. BENJAMIN, INC. ▪ New York, Amsterdam

1966

DISCARD
WEST HILLS COLLEGE LIBRARY
COALINGA, CALIFORNIA
AUG 18'70

INTRODUCTION TO STEREOCHEMISTRY

Copyright © 1965 by W. A. Benjamin, Inc.
All rights reserved

Library of Congress Catalog Card Number 65–10941
Manufactured in the United States of America

The manuscript was put into production on June 25, 1964; this volume was published on April 15, 1965; second printing with corrections January 10, 1966

W. A. BENJAMIN, INC., *New York 10016*

■ EDITOR'S FOREWORD

UNDERGRADUATE EDUCATION in chemistry is in the midst of a major revolution. Sophisticated material, including extensive treatments of current research problems, is increasingly being introduced into college chemistry courses. In organic chemistry, this trend is apparent in the new "elementary" textbooks. However, it has become clear that a single text, no matter how sophisticated, is not the best medium for presenting glimpses of advanced material in addition to the necessary basic chemistry. A spirit of critical evaluation of the evidence is essential in an advanced presentation, while "basic" material must apparently be presented in a relatively dogmatic fashion.

Accordingly, we have instituted a series of short monographs intended as supplements to a first-year organic text; they may, of course, be used either concurrently or subsequently. It is our hope that teachers of beginning organic chemistry courses will supplement the usual text with one or more of these intermediate level monographs and that they may find use in secondary courses as well. In general, the books are designed to be read independently by the interested student and to lead him into the current research literature. It is hoped that they will serve their intended educational purpose and will help the student to recognize organic chemistry as the vital and exciting field it is.

We welcome any comments or suggestions about the series.

New York, New York   RONALD BRESLOW
December, 1964

▪ PREFACE

MOLECULAR SHAPE, form, and symmetry play a central role in organic chemistry. This book is designed as a short introduction to the conceptual basis of stereochemistry. Emphasis has been placed on the fundamentals of *structural* stereochemistry, as distinct from the dynamic aspects that are more appropriately discussed in the context of reaction mechanisms.

The book is divided into three major sections, dealing with (1) structure and symmetry, (2) stereoisomerism, and (3) the separation and configuration of stereoisomers. The following paragraphs briefly touch on some features of the contents.

In the first section, the student is provided with some feeling for molecular architecture. We consider the ways in which the coordination number of carbon determines bonding geometry and then develop the subject by relating empirical bonding geometries to the hybridization of the central carbon atom. The concept of hybridization, certainly no more than a convenient mathematical fiction, has nevertheless permeated much of the recent literature, and I have included it here without presenting alternative and more "physical" views. This task could be left to the lecturer. The student is introduced at the very beginning to a nonrigorous treatment of symmetry elements and later to point groups, with particular emphasis on the presence or absence of reflection symmetry. I believe that this approach is most appealing from the point of view of the organic chemist. Following an excursion into the consequences of molecular deformations (as expressed by the relation between changes in geometry and the accompanying changes in energy), the first section is concluded with a brief discussion of the usefulness and limitations of molecular models.

In the second section, I have adopted the view that stereoisomers are most conveniently classified according to (1) symmetry properties and (2) the nature of the barriers that separate the stereoisomers. Consequently, some of the old terms have been given broader meanings (e.g., diastereomer) while others have been given wide berth (e.g., optical isomer). Stereochemistry is an old science (Louis Pasteur was its first practitioner) and terminology has not kept pace with the development of substantive matter. In the present treatment, new terminology and coinages have been freely introduced. In this section, I have also discussed at some length the dependence of optical activity on structure because I believe that this relationship (or at least some features thereof), despite its essential complexity, can in many cases be qualitatively discussed in terms of the powerful viewpoint introduced by A. Moscowitz and W. Moffitt. The second section concludes with a discussion of topological isomerism. The tenets of conformational analysis, introduced early in the book, are applied throughout.

In the third section, I have tried to emphasize the conceptual basis of asymmetric syntheses and kinetic resolutions, and I have classified these reactions in a way that will aid in the systematic exposition of the subject material.

The exercises appended to each of the major sections are designed not only to test understanding of the preceding material but, through the inclusion of new subject matter, to advance the student beyond the descriptive material. Accordingly, the exercises are an integral part of the text; answers are provided.

Because a more complete coverage of the subject has not been possible, many ideas have been presented in abbreviated and simplified form. The student who wishes to go beyond this book is referred to the texts and articles given in the Bibliography at the end of this book.

It is a pleasure to acknowledge the help and stimulation received over the years from my colleagues at New York University. I also owe a debt of gratitude to Professor Jerome A. Berson, who read the whole manuscript and gave me the benefit of his criticism; many of his suggestions have been incorporated in the final version. I am obliged to Professor Hans Wynberg for permission to include his unpublished results on ethylpropylbutylhexylmethane. Dr. Arnold J. Gordon kindly helped in the critical proofreading of the manuscript.

KURT MISLOW

Princeton, N.J.
September 1964

▪ CONTENTS

EDITOR'S FOREWORD *v*
PREFACE *vii*

1. **STRUCTURE AND SYMMETRY**   **1**

    1–1 Introduction   1
    1–2 Bonding Geometries in Carbon Compounds   6
    1–3 Bonding Orbitals in Carbon Compounds   13
    1–4 Reflection Symmetry—Point Groups   23
    1–5 Molecular Deformations and Strain Energies   33
    1–6 Molecular Models   42
    1–7 Exercises   46

2. **STEREOISOMERISM**   **50**

    2–1 Classification of Structural Isomerism—Enantio-meric and Diastereomeric Relationships   50
    2–2 Optical Activity   54
    2–3 Diastereomers and Racemic Forms   67
    2–4 Torsional Stereoisomerism   70

2–5   Stereoisomerism Resulting from Asymmetric
      Atoms—Designation of Configuration at
      Asymmetric Atoms   86
2–6   Torsional Stereoisomerism in the Presence of
      Asymmetric Atoms   97
2–7   Macromolecules   102
2–8   Topological Isomerism   110
2–9   Exercises   111

3. SEPARATION AND CONFIGURATION OF
    STEREOISOMERS   119

3–1   Separation of Enantiomers and Diastereomers   119
3–2   Optical Activation   120
3–3   Asymmetric Synthesis and Kinetic Resolution   122
3–4   Absolute Configuration   141
3–5   Configurational Correlations by Chemical
      Methods   143
3–6   Configurational Correlations by Physical
      Methods   149
3–7   Exercises   161

      ANSWERS TO EXERCISES   *169*

      BIBLIOGRAPHY   *175*

      INDEX   *179*

1

▪ STRUCTURE AND SYMMETRY

1–1   Introduction

MOLECULAR *structure* is a description of the arrangement or distribution of particles in a molecule. We shall elaborate this definition by explaining our use of the terms *description* and *particles*. A description may take many forms. It may be verbal, or it may be visual—as, for example, through the use of molecular models. The most accurate descriptions are also the most complex: These are the equations which describe the motion of the particles as a function of time and spatial position.

There are two kinds of submolecular particles which are of interest to the organic chemist: the electrons and the nuclei. Wavemechanical arguments lead to a description of electronic structure as a probability distribution of negative charge, i.e., as a smeared-out charge density cloud. In contrast, the distribution of nuclei in space may be discussed more nearly in classical terms, i.e., we may think of nuclei as particles which vibrate with a very small amplitude around well-defined average positions in space. These vibrations are completely analogous to the quivers executed by two weights connected by a spring: the coulombic and exchange

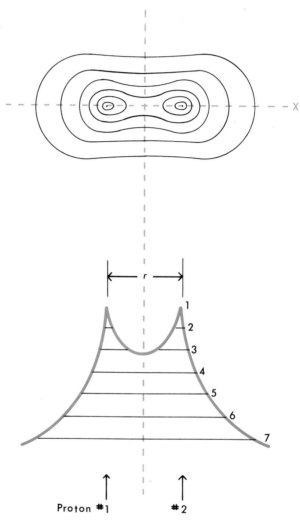

FIGURE 1–1

Schematic representation of electron probability contours in the hydrogen molecule. Electronic charge density decreases in the order $1 > 2$ . . . > 7. Bond length $= r$. Internuclear axis $= x$. Above: plane of symmetry through molecule $=$ cross section. Below: plot of electron density against distance along x.

forces in the molecule simply take the place of the mechanical restoring force in the spring.

Compared to organic molecules, the hydrogen molecule is an extraordinarily simple one (in fact, except for its positive ion [H_2^+], it is the simplest polyatomic molecule conceivable). It might therefore be appropriate to begin our discussion of structure and symmetry by analyzing the case of the hydrogen molecule. In the formation of that molecule, two protons and two electrons have been brought together. The electrons distribute themselves so that the position of the protons assumes an equilibrium value. This distribution of protons and electrons is indicated in Figure 1–1, which shows a cross section of the molecule made by a plane which contains the nuclei. This plane shows contour lines of equal electronic charge density, and the three-dimensional contour surfaces may be developed by rotation around the internuclear line x. Note that well-defined positions are assigned to the protons, whereas the electrons can only be described in terms of the over-all charge density. The molecule may be pictured as a roughly cigar-shaped region of electron density within which the two protons are buried. As shown by the contour lines, the density is highest at points on the x-axis corresponding to the positions of the nuclei, falls off at all distances, but remains high in the region between the nuclei. This region of electron localization between the nuclei coincides in direction with the internuclear line. The outermost contour line shown in diagrams such as these is conventionally chosen to enclose in the neighborhood of 95% of the electron cloud, that is: the probability of finding the electron or electrons within the outermost contour is about 95%.

This description of the distribution of two electrons in the field of the two protons corresponds to the bonding molecular orbital (MO) of hydrogen molecule.

The protons jiggle about but maintain an equilibrium distance r, the *bond length*. The bond length (10.74 Å in this case) refers to the molecular configuration of the vibrating system at a potential energy minimum. The potential energy of the molecule is raised whenever the bond is stretched (say to 10.75 Å) or compressed (say to 10.73 Å), very much as in the analogous case of the two vibrating weights connected by a spring.

We shall now consider symmetry in simple molecules. Every molecule may be classified according to its symmetry, and each particular symmetry class is characterized by the number and type of *symmetry elements* present in such a molecule. For our immediate purposes, the most important such elements are *planes of symmetry*, symbolized by σ, and *simple* (or *proper*) *axes of rotation of order n* (*n-fold axes of symmetry*), symbolized by C_n.

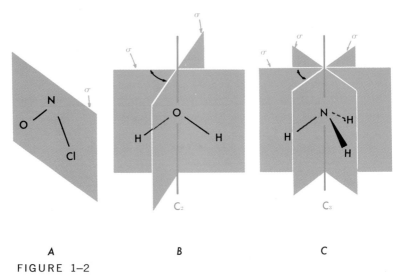

A   **B**   **C**

FIGURE 1–2

A molecule with a single plane of symmetry: nitrosyl chloride (A). *Two molecules with single axes of symmetry: water* (B) *and ammonia* (C). *One of the dihedral angles is shown.*

A σ plane is defined as a mirror plane which bisects a geometric figure so that the half of the figure on one side of the plane is exactly mirrored by the half on the other side. Objects like idealized forks, spoons, hammers, and cups have just one plane of symmetry, and so do molecules like nitrosyl chloride (Figure 1–2), bromocyclopropane and vinyl chloride. A C_n axis is defined as an axis which passes through the molecule so that, by a rotation of $360°/n$ around this axis, a three-dimensional arrangement is obtained which is indistinguishable from the original. For example, water has a twofold axis of symmetry and ammonia a threefold axis, as indicated in Figure 1–2. It is important to note that planes and axes of symmetry are often both encountered in the same molecule. For example, while nitrosyl chloride does not have an axis of symmetry (the trivial one-fold axis C_1 is never considered), water and ammonia have, respectively, two and three planes of symmetry (Figure 1–2) which intersect at the C_n axis. The angles between the planes, the *dihedral angles,* have the values $90°$ and $60°$ for water and ammonia, respectively.

Let us now apply a similar analysis to the case of the hydrogen molecule. It is readily seen (Figure 1–3A) that there exists an

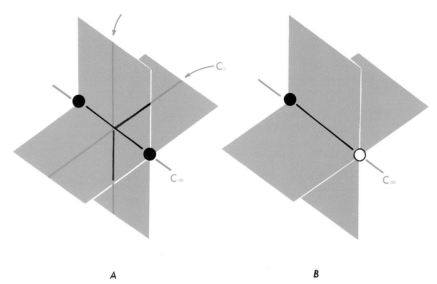

FIGURE 1–3

Some symmetry elements in diatomic molecules. Molecules with cylindrical symmetry have an infinite number of planes of symmetry σ (two are shown) which intersect at the internuclear axis C_∞ (A), and the same is true of molecules with conical symmetry (B). Cylindrically symmetrical molecules also have a plane of symmetry perpendicular to C_∞ which contains an infinite number of twofold axes C_2, two of which are shown in A.

infinite number of σ planes which are identical with the cross section shown in Figure 1–1 and which intersect at the internuclear axis. This axis, which is called the *cylindrical axis,* is also C_∞ because an infinitesimal rotation suffices to transform the new position into one indistinguishable from the original. In addition to the above-mentioned planes there also exists a σ plane which is perpendicular to the internuclear axis, which bisects the molecule, and which contains an infinite number of C_2 axes. Molecules such as oxygen and carbon dioxide have that kind of symmetry which is called *cylindrical symmetry.* Objects such as idealized hourglasses, footballs (American), and doughnuts also have cylindrical symmetry. *Conical symmetry* is a closely related kind of axial symmetry. In molecules possessing conical symmetry, e.g., hydrogen chloride, there also exists an infinite number of σ planes which intersect at the internuclear axis C_∞. However, we now have no σ plane and no C_2 axes which are perpendicular to the C_∞ axis (Figure 1–3B). Objects like idealized funnels, saucers, soda bottles, pins, and eggs have conical symmetry. Cylindrically and conically symmetrical objects have *one* C_∞ axis. The only object possessing more than one such axis is the sphere, which has an infinite number of C_∞ axes intersecting at the center (*spherical symmetry*). We shall elaborate on the subject of symmetry elements in Section 1–4.

1–2   Bonding Geometries in Carbon Compounds

Although molecules containing carbon are far more complex than the hydrogen molecule, a description of bonding in organic molecules may be approached in fundamentally the same manner. A carbon nucleus, one or more other nuclei, and the appropriate number of electrons are brought together, and the electrons are allowed to distribute themselves in a fashion which stabilizes the equilibrium configuration of all the nuclei.   As in hydrogen molecules, there exist regions of high electron density between the nuclei which generally coincide in direction with the internuclear lines. The atoms thus bonded to the central carbon atom are called *ligand atoms*.   The nonbonding electrons, e.g., the three pairs of nonbonding electrons in chloromethane or the lone pair in trimethylamine, give rise to additional regions of high electron density in the molecule.

The number of ligand atoms defines the *coordination number*. Carbon in its various stable combinations may exhibit coordination numbers varying from one to four.   We shall discuss the geometry of bonding separately for each coordination number.

COORDINATION NUMBER ONE   This coordination number is exhibited by cyanide ion and carbon monoxide.   These molecules have conical symmetry and in that respect resemble hydrogen chloride.

COORDINATION NUMBER TWO   In triatomic molecules—and carbon with a coordination number of two implies a minimum of three atoms in the molecule—our description of bonding geometry must take into account two factors. First, the ligand atoms may be equivalent or they may be nonequivalent. Second, the molecular array may be linear or nonlinear. As it happens, the latter question rarely arises in practice, for stable compounds of carbon in which carbon exhibits a coordination number of two are linear. The angle between the bonds is 180°.

Carbon dioxide is a linear molecule in which the ligand atoms are equivalent and in which the bond lengths are equal (1.16Å). Carbonyl sulfide, hydrogen cyanide, and acetylene are linear molecules in which the ligand atoms are not equivalent and in which the two bond lengths of carbon must therefore be different. Carbon suboxide contains one carbon atom with two equivalent ligands and two carbon atoms with different ligands (see Formula I).

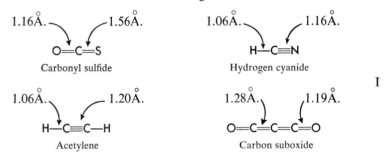

1.16Å. ——— —1.56Å.

O=C=S

Carbonyl sulfide

1.06Å. ——— —1.16Å.

H—C≡N

Hydrogen cyanide

1.06Å. ——— — 1.20Å.

H—C≡C—H

Acetylene

1.28Å. ——— 1.19Å.

O=C=C=C=O

Carbon suboxide

I

It may be noted that carbon dioxide, carbon suboxide, and acetylene have the cylindrical symmetry of hydrogen molecule, while hydrogen cyanide and carbonyl sulfide have the conical symmetry of hydrogen chloride.

COORDINATION NUMBER THREE   Since four atoms need not lie in one plane, combinations of carbon with three ligand atoms raises for the first time the question of *nonplanarity*. However, with the exception of carbanions (and possibly radicals), in which the unshared electrons may be regarded as occupying an additional position on the coordination sphere, the most stable groupings containing carbon bonded to three atoms are planar, and our discussion is therefore considerably simplified.

Groupings of this type in which carbon is attached to three identical ligands (as in graphite) are quite exceptional. Other than carbonate ion, the only common members in this group of compounds are the carbonium ions R_3C^+, of which the methyl

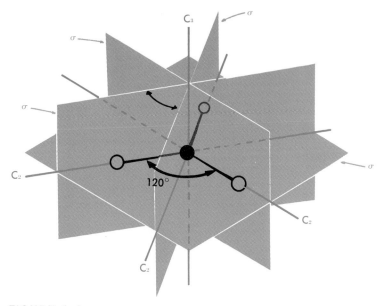

FIGURE 1–4

> *Trigonal symmetry illustrated by methyl cation, showing the four σ-planes, the three C_2 axes, the C_3 axis, one of the three trigonal bond angles (heavy arrow), and one of the dihedral angles (light arrow). Black circle = carbon atom; open circle = hydrogen atom.*

cation (CH_3^+) is the simplest representative. Methyl cation has *trigonal symmetry,* the chief attributes of which are summarized in Figure 1–4. The three ligands are completely equivalent in space and it is easily seen that the bond angles of such arrays must be 120°. However, in the vast majority of compounds containing tricoordinate carbon, the carbon atom is attached to nonequivalent ligands. Hence, the totality of the interactions of the three ligands (including nuclei, bonding, and nonbonding electrons) with each other no longer has regular trigonal symmetry (Figure 1–5). Because the distribution of electrons around the central carbon atom now does not have regular trigonal symmetry, the three bond angles cannot be 120°. In other words, even if the bond angles in such cases were experimentally found to be 120°, such an observation would merely indicate that the differences in the interactions of the three ligands are very slight, and therefore that the differences

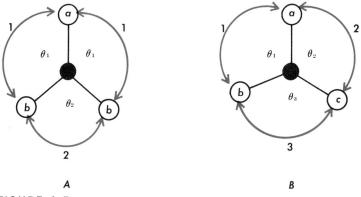

A   **B**

FIGURE 1–5

*Illustration of a symmetry argument. Numbered arrows indicate inter-
action of ligands* a, b, *and* c *attached to carbon (black circle). In A,
two ligands (b) are equivalent and two of the interactions (labeled 1)
and bond angles (Θ_1) are therefore identical and different from the third
(except in cases of* $\mathbf{D}_{6h}$ *symmetry). In B the three ligands are all nonequivalent and the three interactions and bond angles must therefore be
different. All four atoms are in one plane.*

in the bond angles are extremely small. It cannot be doubted
that such differences, though they might perhaps be too small
to be observable with currently available measuring techniques,
would nevertheless be finite and could in principle be detected
by more sensitive devices.

Actually the differences in the bond angles are usually large
enough to be detected, and a few examples can be adduced
(Formula II):

Formaldehyde   Phosgene   Ethylene   Acetyl chloride

II

One exception to the generalization implicit in Figure 1–5A is
the case of a molecule having $\mathbf{D}_{6h}$ symmetry (section 1–4), such as
benzene (Formula III):

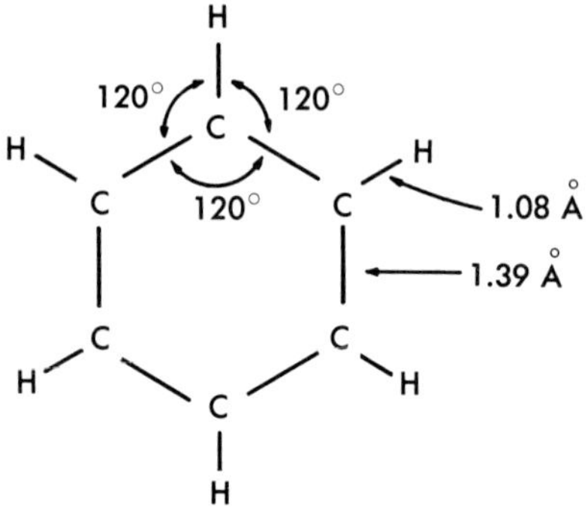

Benzene

III

This planar array of twelve atoms has perfect hexagonal symmetry (i.e., it contains a C_6 axis perpendicular to the plane of the paper which is also a σ plane) and *all* the bond angles are precisely 120°. Another example is the inner ring in coronene (Formula IV):

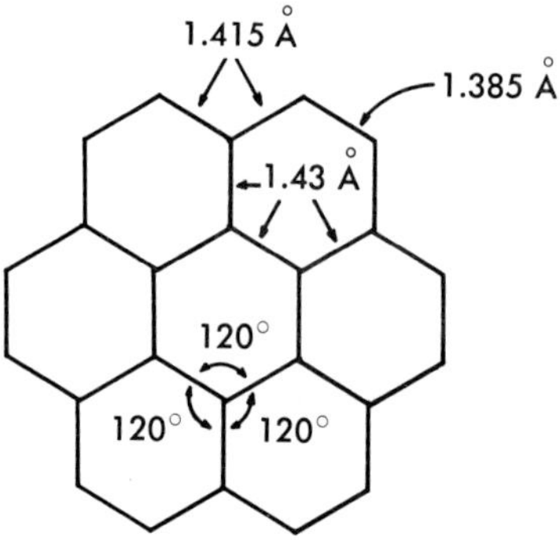

Coronene

IV

Symmetry arguments such as these are extremely useful in stereochemical discussions. It must be re-emphasized that the nature and magnitude of the electronic interactions are completely immaterial to the validity of such arguments and become important only when we attempt to predict or justify the direction and magnitude of the observed effects.

COORDINATION NUMBER FOUR   Groupings of this type, in which carbon is attached to four ligands, are the ones most commonly encountered in organic chemistry. In diamond these ligands are identical. As shown by a great variety of physical measurements, the atoms attached to carbon in compounds of type CX_4 are completely equivalent. Examples of such compounds are (Formula V):

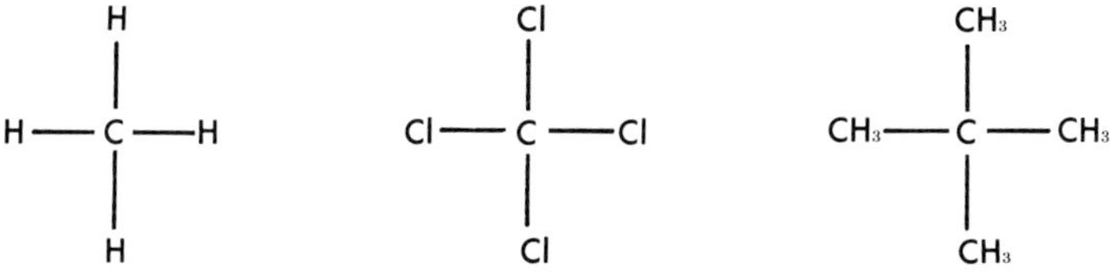

$$
\begin{array}{ccc}
\text{H} & \text{Cl} & \text{CH}_3 \\
| & | & | \\
\text{H}\!-\!\text{C}\!-\!\text{H} & \text{Cl}\!-\!\text{C}\!-\!\text{Cl} & \text{CH}_3\!-\!\text{C}\!-\!\text{CH}_3 \\
| & | & | \\
\text{H} & \text{Cl} & \text{CH}_3
\end{array}
\qquad \text{V}
$$

Methane   Carbon tetrachloride   Neopentane (central carbon only)

Equivalence in three dimensions means that a molecule of the type CX_4 has only one X—C—X angle and only one X—X internuclear distance. A square planar array of four X groups with a carbon atom at the center does not meet these specifications. It may be shown that equivalence in three dimensions signifies *regular tetrahedral symmetry,* an analysis of which is given in Figure 1–6. This figure shows a carbon atom, called the *tetrahedral carbon atom,* attached to four hydrogen atoms numbered 1 through 4. Inspection of the figure shows that there are four C_3 axes, one for each of the C—H bonds. In this respect we are reminded of the case of ammonia (Figure 1–2C). Each of the four C_3 axes in methane is the locus of intersection of three σ planes, so that one might expect a total of twelve planes: However, each of the σ planes contains two C_3 axes, so that there are actually only six σ planes. These six planes may be ordered into the three pairs shown in Figure 1–6. In each pair the two planes are perpendicular to each other and they intersect to form a C_2 axis. The three resulting C_2 axes are mutually perpendicular, and they bisect the six tetrahedral angles.

The value of the regular tetrahedral angle is arc cos $-\frac{1}{3}$. Expressed in degrees, this is approximately 109.5°.

As soon as the ligands are no longer equivalent, the regular tetrahedral symmetry vanishes since the various interactions of the ligands around the central carbon are no longer identical. It follows that the bond angles can also no longer be 109.5°. The conclusion of this symmetry argument is borne out by numerous

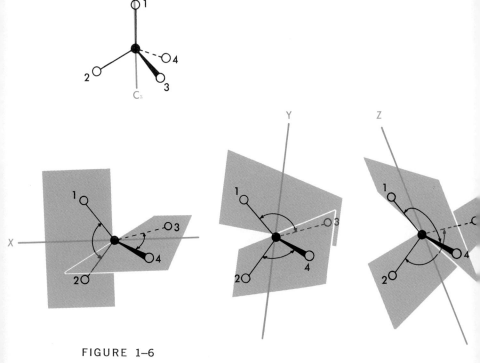

FIGURE 1–6

Tetrahedral symmetry illustrated by methane, showing one of the four C_3 axes, the six σ planes, the three mutually perpendicular C_2 axes (x, y and z), and the six tetrahedral angles. Black circle = carbon atom; open circle = hydrogen atom.

experimental observations. Two examples are given below (Formula VI):

Methyl fluoride   Methylene fluoride

Even in acyclic hydrocarbons, such as propane and n-butane, the C—C—C bond angle is approximately 112°, not 109.5°. *The regular tetrahedral angle is therefore the exception rather than the rule in organic chemistry.*

1–3   **Bonding Orbitals in Carbon Compounds**

When atoms are brought together to form a molecule, the electrons and nuclei interact. The electronic distributions in the atoms (i.e., the atomic orbitals or AO's) are perturbed. We say that the AO's *overlap.* The charge density distribution in the localized bonding MO bears a relationship to the charge density distribution in the original AO's, and it is therefore customary to discuss the localized bonding MO with reference to the AO's which would result at infinite separation of the nuclei. For example, in the case of hydrogen molecule the bonding MO may be mathematically described in terms of the component hydrogen AO's.

A discussion of localized bonding orbitals in carbon compounds is rendered far more complex by the fact that carbon has four low-lying AO's which are available for bonding, whereas hydrogen has only one (i.e., $1s$). These four orbitals are the $2s$ and the three $2p$ orbitals. In its lowest energy state, the carbon atom has two electrons in the $2s$ orbital and two electrons in the $2p$ orbitals, so that the description of the electron configuration is $1s^2 2s^2 p^2$. A slightly higher energy state is described by $1s^2 2sp^3$, where one electron occupies each of the four AO's. Like all s-orbitals, the $2s$-orbital is spherically symmetrical and has its highest charge density at the nucleus. Each p-orbital, however, is cylindrically symmetrical, and the charge density at the nucleus is zero. The three p-orbitals differ only in direction in space and the three cylindrical axes define a Cartesian coordinate system (x, y, and z). The σ planes which are perpendicular to the cylindrical axes (i.e., yz, xz, and xy, respectively) define the regions of zero electron density and are the *nodal surfaces.* Figure 1–7*A* shows projected contour lines of equal electronic charge density for the $2p_z$ AO. The three-dimensional contour surfaces may be developed by rotation around the C_∞ axis z. It is seen that the charge density is concentrated in the *lobes,* two separated distorted ellipsoids which float above and below the nodal xy-plane.

If these AO's were directly developed into bonding orbitals, tetra-coordinate carbon would have three equivalent bonds at right angles to each other, and a fourth nonequivalent bond. This does not correspond to any experimentally observed geometry of carbon

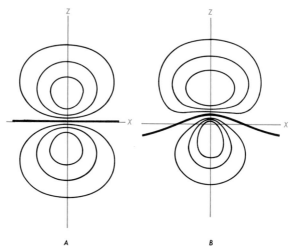

FIGURE 1–7

A, *schematic representation of contours for the* $2p_z$ *atomic orbital in the* xz *plane. The* xy *plane is the nodal surface (heavy line) and the nucleus is at the origin of the coordinate system.* B, *schematic representation of contours for a* $2(s + \lambda p)$ *atomic orbital in the* xz *plane. The nodal surface (heavy line) is seen edgewise, and the nucleus is at the origin of the coordinate system.*

bonding orbitals. It follows, therefore, that the wave function (i.e., the mathematical description of the motion and distribution of an electron in the field of the nucleus) of the bonding AO's must be different from the wave functions of the AO's of unbonded carbon.

This difficulty is overcome by a mathematical description of the bonding AO's as various linear combinations of the $2s$ and $2p$ AO's in carbon $1s^2 2sp^3$. The bonding orbital is now called a *hybrid orbital* and the process of linear combination is called "hybridization" or "mixing" of "contributing" AO's (LCAO). The AO's included in the LCAO are the $2s$-orbital, plus one, two, or three $2p$-orbitals. Each bonding AO may therefore be represented by $s + \lambda_i p$, where λ_i is the *mixing coefficient* or *hybridization parameter* for the *i* th bonding AO and is a measure of the extent to which the $2p$ AO contributes to the hybrid AO. The condition which is imposed on λ_i is that (Eq. 1–1)

$$\sum_i \frac{1}{1 + \lambda_i^2} = 1 \qquad (1\text{--}1)$$

The fraction $1/(1 + \lambda_i^2)$ is the *s-character* of the *i th* bonding AO and the above equation simply states that the sum total of the fractional *s*-contributions of the individual hybrid AO's must add up to one 2*s* AO. Similarly, the sum total of the fractional *p*-contributions of the individual hybrid AO's must add up to the number of *p*-orbitals mixed in (Eq. 1–2)

$$\sum_i \frac{\lambda_i^2}{1 + \lambda_i^2} = 1, 2, \text{ or } 3 \qquad (1\text{--}2)$$

where $\lambda_i^2/(1 + \lambda_i^2)$ is the *p*-character of the *i th* bonding AO. Figure 1–7B shows projected contour lines of equal electronic charge density for a hybrid $2(s + \lambda p)$ AO, where λ has generally some value between 1 and $\sqrt{3}$, though the value may fall outside these limits. The three-dimensional contour surfaces may be developed by rotation around the C_∞ axis z. The orbital has conical symmetry. It may be noted that the hybrid orbital betrays its parentage: Like the 2*s* and unlike the 2*p* orbital it has a finite charge density at the nucleus, but unlike the 2*s* and like the 2*p* orbital it has an open nodal surface. The nodal surface, however, is no longer planar and does not pass through the nucleus; instead it is roughly bell-shaped, and the charge density is concentrated in unequal lobes on either side of the nodal surface as schematically shown in cross section of Figure 1–7B. Again like the 2*p* AO's, the $2(s + \lambda p)$ AO's have directionality: This affords better overlap and makes for stronger bonds.

Since the 2*s* orbital has its highest electron density at the nucleus whereas the 2*p* orbital has zero electron density at the nucleus, it follows that the greater the *s*-character of the bonding AO, the greater will be the polarization of electrons toward the nucleus. This theoretical concept permits a number of correlations of physical properties, but to the student of stereochemistry the most important consequence of hybridization is the change of bond angle with *s*- or *p*-character. In the following highly simplified treatment, the approximation is made that the bonding orbitals are directed along the internuclear lines, i.e., are not bent away from them, and that each hybrid orbital is localized so that we may neglect interactions between adjacent bonds and bonded atoms. This approximation is in fact not always satisfactory. Nevertheless, for the present purposes we shall adhere to this simplification except in the case of cyclic molecules, where we shall introduce the concept of bent bonds. When the *p*-character of two orbitals on a carbon atom is 100% ($\lambda = \infty$), the bond angle is 90° (i.e., pure $2p$ AO's); when the *p*-character is 50% ($\lambda = 1$) the bond angle is 180°. A simple equation (Eq. 1–3) correlates θ_{ij}, the angle subtended by two bonding AO's *i* and *j*:

$$1 + \lambda_i \lambda_j \cos \theta_{ij} = 0 \qquad (1\text{–}3)$$

For identical ligands ($i = j$) (Eq. 1–4):

$$1 + \lambda_i^2 \cos \theta_{ii} = 0 \qquad (1\text{–}4)$$

Thus, with increasing *p*-character, the bond angle decreases. It is conventional to express the *p*-character of the *i* th AO by λ_i^2, which might be called the *hybridization index* and is indicated as a superscript (e.g., $sp^{1.6}$ if $\lambda_i^2 = 1.6$).

The mathematical process of hybridization requires detailed knowledge of the various energy terms which are involved in the interaction of the ligand AO's with the central carbon atom and with each other. In general, such knowledge is not available, and the hybridization index is therefore determined by reference to physical properties which depend on the molecular parameters of bond length, bond angle, bond energy, bond stretching force constant, and bond moment. Bond angles and bond lengths may be determined directly by X-ray or electron diffraction. In the case of molecules containing carbon bonded to hydrogen, the acid strength and especially the NMR ^{13}C—H spin-spin coupling constant (J_{CH}) are additional measures of the hybridization of the carbon bonding orbital; note the empirical relationship (Eq. 1–5).

$$J_{CH} \text{ (cps)} = \frac{500}{1 + \lambda_i^2} \qquad (1\text{–}5)$$

The only molecules in which recourse to experimental data is unnecessary are those in which the carbon atom is bonded to equivalent ligands. In that case there can only be one bond angle θ_{ii}, and λ_i^2 follows directly from the value of that angle. Thus, in tetracoordinate carbon this value is arc cos $- \frac{1}{3}$ and all three $2p$ AO's are mixed; $\lambda_i^2 = 3$ and the four bonding AO's are sp_{xyz}^3. In tricoordinate carbon, θ_{ii} is arc cos $- \frac{1}{2}$; $\lambda_i^2 = 2$ and the three bonding AO's are sp^2. In this case only two $2p$ AO's are mixed ($2p_x$ and $2p_y$); these define the plane (xy) of the three sp_{xy}^2 orbitals, whereas the third unmixed $2p_z$ AO has its cylindrical axis at right angles to that plane. Finally, in dicoordinate carbon, θ_{ii} is arc cos $- 1$, $\lambda_i^2 = 1$, and the two bonding AO's are sp_x; only one $2p_x$ AO is mixed, thus defining the linear coordinate (x) of the hybrid AO's, whereas the two unmixed ($2p_y + 2p_z$) AO's parallel the plane (yz) at right angles to that line.

Bonds formed by carbon are denoted as *σ-bonds* or *π-bonds*. The former are cylindrically or conically symmetrical MO's and are formed by an axial or head-on approach of two p (or $s + \lambda p$) AO's or by axial overlap of a p (or $s + \lambda p$) AO and a spherically symmetrical AO such as the hydrogen $1s$-orbital. π-Orbitals are formed by parallel, sideways overlap of two $2p$ AO's. These statements are illustrated by the schematic diagrams in Figure 1–8.

We are now prepared for a description of the bonding geometry and the bonding orbitals of most common organic molecules. For example, methane consists of a carbon nucleus which is tetrahedrally surrounded by four protons; the regions of highest electron density are found at the nuclei and along the internuclear lines. These regions correspond to the σ-bonds which are formed by overlap of carbon $2sp^3$ and hydrogen $1s$ electrons.

We recall that regular tetrahedral symmetry obtains only with four equivalent ligands, and the structural analysis of other than tetrahedrally symmetrical tetracoordinate carbon compounds is therefore rather more involved. If only one ligand is different (Cab_3), there are only two different angles, θ_{ii} and θ_{ij}. These are related by the expression $3 \sin^2 \theta_{ij} = 2(1 - \cos \theta_{ii})$. From the expression $1 + \lambda_i^2 \cos \theta_{ii} = 0$ one may calculate λ_i^2, and λ_j^2 may then be obtained from the condition for total s-character, $3/(1 + \lambda_i)^2 + 1/(1 + \lambda_j^2) = 1$. If there are two pairs of ligands (Ca_2b_2), there will be three angles to consider, θ_{ii}, θ_{jj}, and θ_{ij}; the last is related to the others by the expression $\cos \theta_{ij} = - \cos \frac{1}{2} \theta_{ii} \cos \frac{1}{2} \theta_{jj}$. Again λ_i^2 may be calculated from the equation $1 + \lambda_i^2 \cos \theta_{ii} = 0$, and λ_j^2 from the condition for total s-character, $2/(1 + \lambda_i^2) + 2/(1 + \lambda_j^2) = 1$. For example, the C—C—C angle in propane (θ_{ii}) is $112°$, whence $\lambda_i^2 = 2.7$. From the conditions for total s-char-

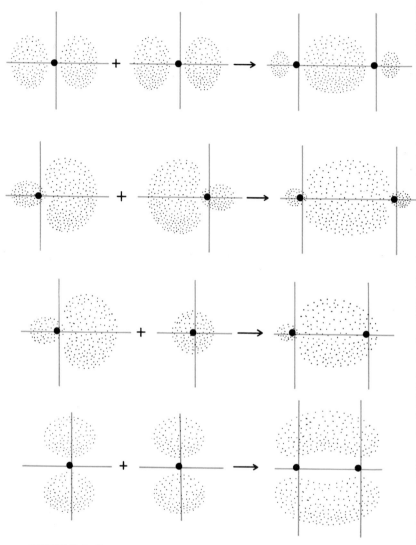

FIGURE 1–8

Schematic representation of σ- and π-bonds. On the right are indicated the bonding MO's formed from the AO's on the left. Top: axial approach of two 2p AO's to form a σ-bond. Second from the top: axial approach of two 2(s + λp) AO's to form a σ-bond, e.g., a C—C single bond. Third from the top: axial approach of a 2(s + λp) AO and a 1s AO to form a σ-bond, e.g., a C—H single bond. Bottom: parallel sideways approach of two 2p AO's to form a π-bond.

acter, $\lambda_j^2 = 3.4$, and $\theta_{jj} = 107°$ (the H—C—H bond angle). See also Formula VII.

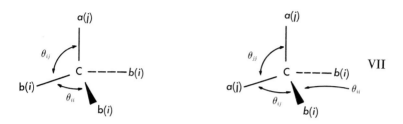

VII

A particularly instructive example is cyclopropane, the simplest alicyclic compound of carbon. This molecule has four σ planes, a C_3 axis and three C_2 axes. The H—C—H angle is about 114°, which means that the C—H bond is described as a σ-bond formed by the overlap of a carbon $sp^{2.5}$ orbital and a hydrogen $1s$ orbital. Two of the carbon hybrid orbitals are $sp^{2.5}$ and the other two must therefore be $sp^{3.7}$, since $2/3.5 + 2/(1 + \lambda^2) = 1.00$, whence $\lambda^2 = 3.7$. Knowing the hybridization index we now calculate that the C—C—C bond angle is 105.5°. Since the three carbon atoms occupy the corners of a regular triangle, however, the angle subtended by the internuclear lines is only 60°. The three $sp^{3.7} - sp^{3.7}$ bonds therefore curve around the outside of the triangle as shown in Figure 1–9A. Such bonds are called *bent bonds, banana bonds* or τ-bonds.

We have delayed until now a definition of the term *bond angle,* for it is not until this point in our discussion that an ambiguity in the meaning of the term has arisen. The physical methods of structure determination, e.g., X-ray and electron diffraction, only give the relative positions of the nuclei in space, and the experimentally determined angles are therefore actually *internuclear angles.* In that sense the *endo* (inner) bond angles in cyclopropane are 60°. However, one might alternatively specify as bond angle the angle subtended by the bonding orbital axes at the nucleus, i.e., the *interorbital angle,* as distinct from the internuclear angle. Some physical methods of structure determination, e.g., NMR (J_{CH}), may be regarded within the framework of current theory to lead to an estimate of this angle.

The τ-bond is thus seen to be intermediate between a pure

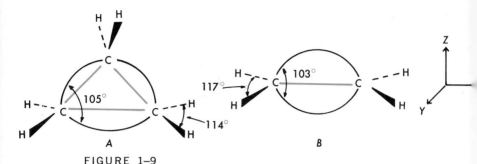

FIGURE 1–9

Illustration of bent bonds. A, cyclopropane; B, ethylene. Internuclear lines in color, direction of bonds in black.

σ- and a pure π-bond. It is not a σ-bond since it lacks cylindrical symmetry, and it is not a π-bond because the bonded nuclei do not lie in a common nodal plane. In σ-bonds the electron density is highest along the internuclear line and the bond is strongest. In π-bonds the electron density vanishes along the internuclear line and the bond is weakest. In bent bonds, both the electron density along the internuclear line and the bond strength assume intermediate values.

In principle, whenever the internuclear line does not lie on a C_n ($n > 1$) axis, bent bonds result. However, especially in acyclic systems, the internuclear and interorbital angles usually differ only slightly and for that reason we generally ignore the distinction. Nevertheless, we should at least be aware of the possibility of curvature of bonds, whose direction does not always coincide with that of the internuclear lines.

In the structural analysis of tricoordinate carbon only two cases of nonequivalent ligands need be considered: Ca_2b and $Cabc$. The Ca_2b case is illustrated by the σ-bonding AO's in ethylene. The H—C—H angle (θ_{ii}) is $117°$, whence $\lambda_i^2 = 2.2$. From the condition of total s-character, i.e., $2/(1 + \lambda_i^2) + 1/(1 + \lambda_j^2) = 1$, the value calculated for λ_j^2 is 1.7. Note that since $\theta_{ij} > \theta_{ii}$, $\lambda_j^2 < \lambda_i^2$. In ethylene the six atoms occupy a σ-plane (xy) which contains the five σ-bonds (one C—C $2sp_{xy}^{1.7} - 2sp_{xy}^{1.7}$ and four C—H $2sp_{xy}^{2.2} - 1s$). This is the σ-framework. The two parallel $2p_z$ orbitals overlap sideways to form a C—C π-bond whose nodal surface is the xy-plane. The C—H σ-bonds in ethylene are single bonds; the C—C σ, π-bond is a double bond.

Alternatively, the double bond may be described as formed by overlap of the identically hybridized AO's of the type Ca_2b_2. The C—H bonds are described as before ($\lambda_i^2 = 2.2$), but now the $2p_z$ orbital does not remain unhybridized. The total s-character of the bonding AO's on each carbon is given by $2/3.2 + 2/(1 + \lambda_j^2) = 1$, whence $\lambda_j^2 = 4.3$. The double bond in this description is simply a double bent bond formed by overlap of two $2sp_{xz}^{4.3}$ AO's on one carbon with two similar AO's on the other, and the interorbital angle between the bent bonds is about $103°$ (Figure 1–9B).

The $Cabc$ case may be illustrated by acetyl chloride. In this case there are three angles θ_{ij}, θ_{jk}, and θ_{ik}, all of which are known (Sec. 1–2), and three mixing coefficients. Solution of the three simultaneous equations $1 + \lambda_i\lambda_j \cos \theta_{ij} = 0$, $1 + \lambda_j\lambda_k \cos \theta_{jk} = 0$, and $1 + \lambda_i\lambda_k \cos \theta_{ik} = 0$ gives values for λ_i^2, λ_j^2, and λ_k^2, which are indicated below (Formula VIII). Note the variation in hybridization indices.

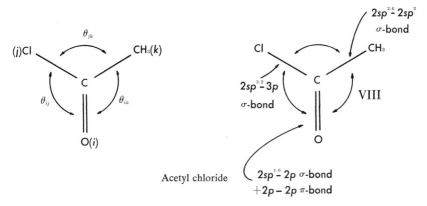

Acetyl chloride

The structural analysis of dicoordinate carbon compounds may be illustrated for the case of acetylene (Cab). The σ-framework is linear and all four atoms lie on a cylindrical axis (x). Three σ-bonds are formed, two by overlap of a carbon $2sp_x^n$ and a hydrogen $1s$ AO, and one by overlap of two $2sp_x^m$ AO's where $nm = 1$ since the condition for linearity is $\lambda_i\lambda_j = 1$. Even though $n \neq m$ unless $i = j$ (Ca_2), it will simplify further discussion to assume $n = m = 1$. The two $2p$-orbitals which are centered on each carbon are mutually perpendicular, and it can be shown that this is equivalent to an orbital description of a doughnut-shaped electron cloud whose nodal "surface" is the C_∞ axis. The two parallel $(2p_y + 2p_z)$-doughnuts overlap sideways to form a cylindrical

π,π-bond which surrounds the σ-bond. This C—C σ,π,π-bond is called a triple bond.

The above descriptions of multiple bonds are useful in discussing the geometry of allenes and cumulenes (Formula IX).

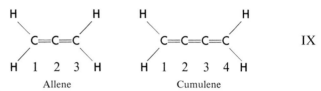

Allene   Cumulene   IX

In allene and cumulene, the end CH_2-groups are comparable to the CH_2-groups in ethylene: The H—C—H angle is $117°$ and the carbon atoms are correspondingly hybridized. The σ-framework of allene is therefore described by four $2sp^{2.2}\text{-}1s$ C—H σ-bonds and two $2sp^{1.7}\text{-}2sp_x$ C—C σ-bonds, the latter forming a linear array (x-axis, C_1—C_2—C_3) since the bond angle of dicoordinate carbon atom 2 is $180°$. The $2p_y$ and $2p_z$ electrons on the central carbon atom 2 cannot overlap cylindrically with the neighboring p-orbitals because each of the end carbon atoms 1 and 3 bears only *one* $2p$-electron, in contrast to the case of acetylene where each of the neighboring atoms carried *two* $(2p_y + 2p_z)$-electrons. Therefore, if the one p-electron on carbon atom 1 is designated $2p_y$, the π-bond formed with carbon atom 2 cannot be cylindrically symmetrical but must be formed by overlap only with the $2p_y$ electron on carbon atom 2. This π-bond must have a nodal surface in the xz-plane. The remaining p-electron on carbon atom 2 is a $2p_z$ electron. If a π-bond is now formed by parallel sideways overlap of that p-electron and the lone p-electron on carbon atom 3, it follows that the latter is necessarily also a $2p_z$ electron. The nodal surface of the second π-bond is therefore in the xy-plane. We have seen that the nodal plane of molecules such as ethylene is also the plane of the σ-framework. It is therefore concluded that the plane formed by H—C_1—H is the xz-plane and that the plane formed by H—C_3—H is the xy-plane, i.e., the two planes are perpendicular to each other.

In cumulene, as in acetylene, each of the two central carbon atoms 2 and 3 carries two $(2p_y + 2p_z)$ electrons. However, since one each of the above-mentioned p-electrons is also engaged in π-bond formation with the p-electrons on end-carbon atoms 1 or 4, no cylindrical π,π-bond can in this case be formed between carbon atoms 2 and 3. Instead, if the p-electron on carbon atom 1 is the

$2p_y$-electron, the π-bond with the electron on carbon atom 2 has its nodal surface in the xz plane, and the remaining $2p_z$-electron on carbon atom 2 must form a π-bond with the corresponding $2p_z$-electron on carbon atom 3. The nodal surface of the second π-bond is the xy plane. The remaining $2p_y$-electron on carbon atom 3 must form a third π-bond with the corresponding $2p_y$-electron on carbon atom 4 whose nodal surface is again the xz plane. It follows that all of the nuclei lie in one plane (xz), i.e., the σ-framework is planar. The σ-bonds are similar to those described for allene: four $2sp_{xz}^{2.2}$-$1s$ C—H σ-bonds, two $2sp_{xz}^{1.7}$-$2sp_x$ C—C σ-bonds, and one $2sp_x$-$2sp_x$ C—C σ-bond between carbon atoms 2 and 3.

In much the same manner we can now provide a structural analysis of other diverse molecules, e.g., formaldehyde and benzene. In formaldehyde the σ-framework is planar (xy) and forms the nodal surface of the C—O π-bond (internuclear line x). We may choose to describe the C—O bond without hybridization of the oxygen AO. Since the H—C—H angle is about $118°$, the C—O double bond is made up of a C—O $2sp_{xy}^{1.8}$-$2p_x$ σ-bond and a C—O $2p_z$-$2p_z$ π-bond. One of the unshared electron pairs occupies the oxygen $2p_y$ orbital and the other the oxygen $2s$ orbital. If we choose to hybridize the oxygen AO, we arrive at a slightly different description: the C—O double bond is now made up of a $2sp_{xy}^{1.8}$-$2sp_{xy}^2$ σ-bond and a $2p_z$-$2p_z$ π-bond, and the two unshared electron pairs occupy the remaining two oxygen $2sp_{xy}^2$ AO's, i.e., they occupy the nodal plane of the π-bond.

In benzene, the σ-framework $(xy$ plane$)$ has hexagonal symmetry. The C—C σ-bonds are described by $2sp_{xy}^2$-$2sp_{xy}^2$ and the C—H σ-bonds by $2sp_{xy}^2$-$1s$. The plane of the σ-framework is the nodal plane of the π-cloud which is formed by sideways overlap of the six p_z electrons.

1–4   Reflection Symmetry—Point Groups

We have made frequent use of symmetry elements in order to aid in the description of molecular geometry, and we shall now introduce a shorthand notation for specifying the symmetry class of the commonly encountered organic molecules. This notation designates the *point group* (i.e., type of symmetry) to which the molecule or object belongs, and we shall discuss in a nonrigorous manner a technique for specifying the point group. The required operations involve three symmetry elements. Two of these, the σ planes and the C_n axes, are already familiar to us. The third is connected with the attribute of *reflection symmetry* (or *mirror symmetry*). An object is said to have reflection symmetry if it is superimposable on its reflection or mirror image. Reflection symmetry is revealed by the presence of a *rotation-reflection axis* (also called *mirror axis, improper axis* or *alternating axis*) S_n: in a molecule having such an axis, reflection in a plane perpendicular to that axis followed by a rotation by $360°/n$ will convert the object into itself. Usually we do not find it necessary to specify this axis, since for our purposes (to decide whether or not the object possesses reflection symmetry) it is generally sufficient merely to compare by visual inspection the identity, i.e., the point-by-point superimposability, of an object and its *mirror image*, i.e., of the figure which results from reflection of the object across the mirror plane.

Before we begin our discussion, we must define the term *conformation*. By conformation we mean a particular geometry of the molecule, i.e., a description of the disposition of atoms in space in terms of bond distances, bond angles, and dihedral angles. Obviously a molecule may have more than one conformation and this may be illustrated by the case of ethane. There are various ways in which the atoms in ethane can be arranged relative to each other, essentially without changing the bond angles and bond lengths but by changing the dihedral angles; some of these are shown in

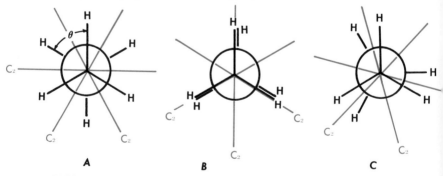

A   **B**   **C**

FIGURE 1–10

Some conformations of ethane in the Newman projection. A, dihedral angle $\theta = 60°$ (staggered); B, dihedral angle $\theta = 0°$ (eclipsed); C, dihedral angle $0° < \theta < 60°$ (skewed). The principal C_3 axes are coincident with the C—C bond and are perpendicular to the plane of the paper.

the end-on Newman projections of Figure 1–10. The conformations which are possible for ethane are three in type (according to dihedral angle): one *staggered* (*A*), one *eclipsed* (*B*), and an infinite number of *skewed* (*C*).

We are now prepared to classify molecular arrangements into point groups. If we restrict our discussion to the more important point groups it is found that molecules (strictly, molecular conformations) may be grouped into five symmetry categories which are based on our three symmetry elements or operations, as follows (point groups indicated in bold-face type):

No Reflection Symmetry (Dissymmetry)

1. No C_n (**C₁**)
2. One or more C_n (**C**ₙ and **D**ₙ)

Reflection Symmetry

1. A σ but no C_n (**C**ₛ)
2. No σ (**S**ₙ)
3. Both σ and C_n (**C**ₙᵥ, **C**ₙₕ, **D**ₙд, **D**ₙₕ, **T**д, **O**ₕ)

Our discussion will follow the order of the above classification.

CONFORMATIONS WITHOUT REFLECTION SYMMETRY   Conformations in this category are called *dissymmetric* or *chiral*. *No dissymmetric conformation can have a σ plane*. The presence of such a plane is therefore a sufficient (but not a necessary) condition for reflection symmetry. If a $C_n(n > 1)$ is also absent, the conformation lacks all symmetry elements (*asymmetry*) and is therefore called *asymmetric* (point group **C₁**). Two examples are given in Figure 1–11. A carbon atom attached to four substituents which differ in the sense that exchange of any two gives a new stereoisomer is called an *asymmetric carbon atom*. Sometimes, *though not always* (see below and section 2–5), this arrangement results in asymmetric molecules, such as *A* in Figure 1–11. Numerous objects are asymmetric, e.g., a foot, a hand, an ear.

Among molecules which possess axial symmetry, i.e., molecules which are dissymmetric but not asymmetric, those with one C_2 (point group **C₂**) are quite commonly encountered. Two examples are given in Figure 1–12. A number of idealized objects have **C₂** symmetry, e.g., a single knot, a pretzel, and a pair of scissors. As illustrated in Figure 1–13, the presence of asymmetric atoms does not preclude **C₂** symmetry, provided that the number of such atoms is even.

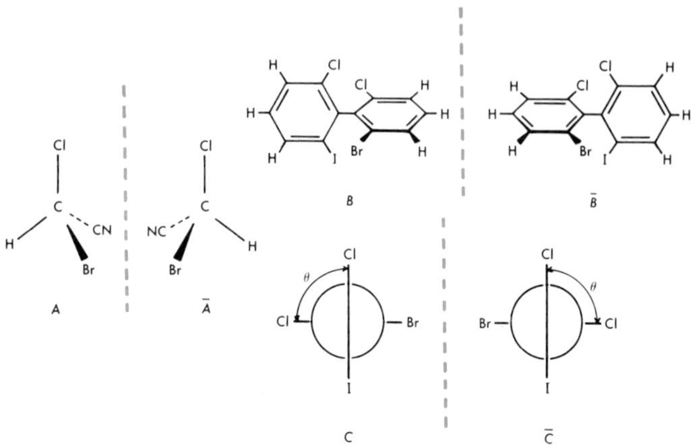

FIGURE 1–11

Some examples of asymmetry (C_1). *A, a molecule containing an asymmetric carbon atom;* $\bar{A}$, *its mirror image.* B, *a twisted biphenyl;* $\bar{B}$, *its mirror image;* C = B *in Newman projection;* $\bar{C}$, *its mirror image.* $\theta =$ *dihedral angle, which may have any value from 0° or 180°. The colored, dashed lines represent the edges of mirror planes at right angles to the plane of the paper.*

A *cylindrical helix* which is *palindromic* also belongs to point group C_2, in contrast to a *conical helix* or screw which belongs to C_1 (Figure 1–14). As here defined, a palindromic cylindrical helix reads the same in either direction along the coil and on the molecular level is exemplified by hexahelicene (Figure 2–10). Non-palindromic cylindrical helices, such as the helical biopolymers in Figures 2–39 and 2–40, belong to point group C_1 and are asymmetric.

Only one example is known to date of a molecule having C_n symmetry of an order higher than two. The unique molecule is tri-*o*-thymotide (Figure 1–15) which has C_3 symmetry.

An object may have a principal C_n axis and in addition may have n C_2 axes in a plane perpendicular to the principal axis. This is called *dihedral symmetry*. In dissymmetric molecules the plane must of course not be a σ plane. Dihedral symmetry in dissymmetric compounds (D_n) is exemplified by the class of doubly bridged biphenyls (Figure 1–16). In these molecules any one of the three C_2 axes is the principal axis and the other two C_2 axes occupy a plane perpendicular to the first. A two-bladed propeller also illustrates D_2 symmetry. Skewed ethane (Figure 1–10C) has D_3 symmetry and so does a three-bladed propeller.

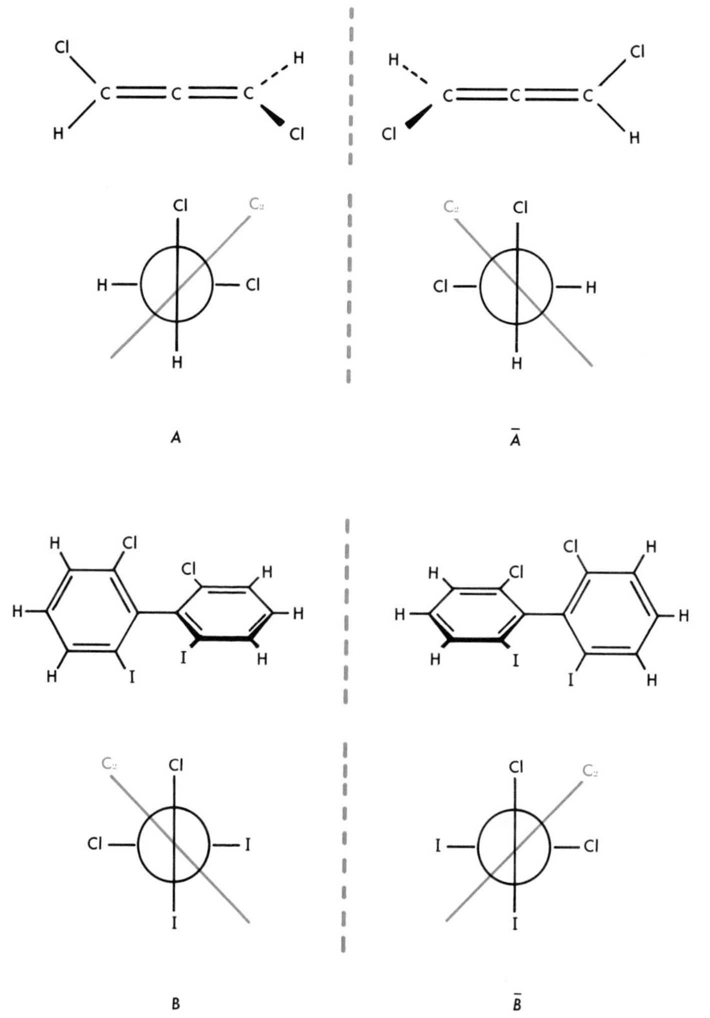

FIGURE 1–12

*Some examples of dissymmetric nonasymmetric molecules (**C**₂). A, an allene; Ā, its mirror image; B, a twisted biphenyl; B̄, its mirror image. The Newman projections in the second and fourth rows correspond to the perspective views in the first and third rows. The C₂ axes are in color and pass through the centers (atoms or bonds) of the molecules.*

CONFORMATIONS WITH REFLECTION SYMMETRY   Conformations in this category are called *nondissymmetric* or *achiral,* terms which are more descriptive than "symmetric." If a nondissymmet-

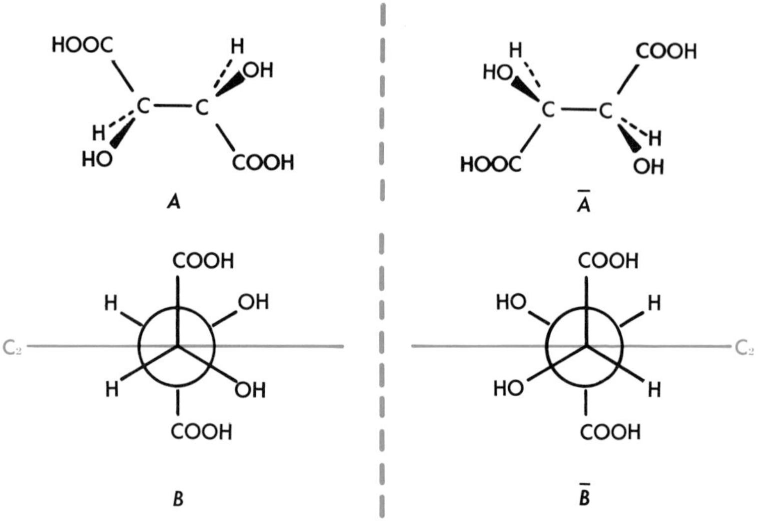

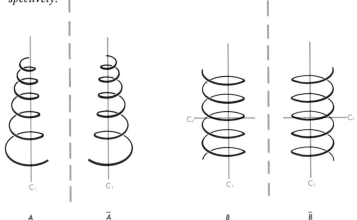

FIGURE 1–13

Example of a dissymmetric nonasymmetric conformation (tartaric acid) containing an even number of asymmetric carbon atoms (C_2). A and Ā are mirror images; B and B̄ are Newman projections of A and Ā, respectively.

FIGURE 1–14

Sections of a conical and a cylindrical helix. Both are dissymmetric. The long axis is C_1. The conical helix (C_1) is asymmetric but the cylindrical helix (C_2) is not since there is a C_2 at right angles to the long axis and through the midpoint of the coil. A and Ā are mirror image forms of the conical helix; B and B̄ are mirror image forms of the cylindrical helix.

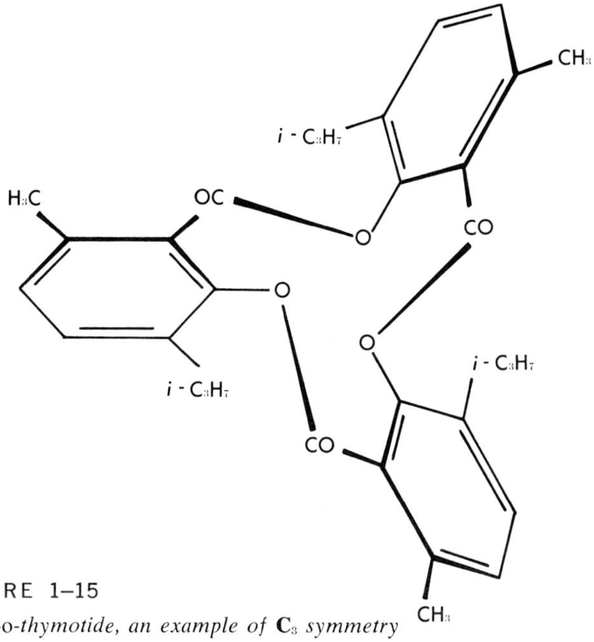

FIGURE 1–15

Tri-o-thymotide, an example of **C**₃ *symmetry*

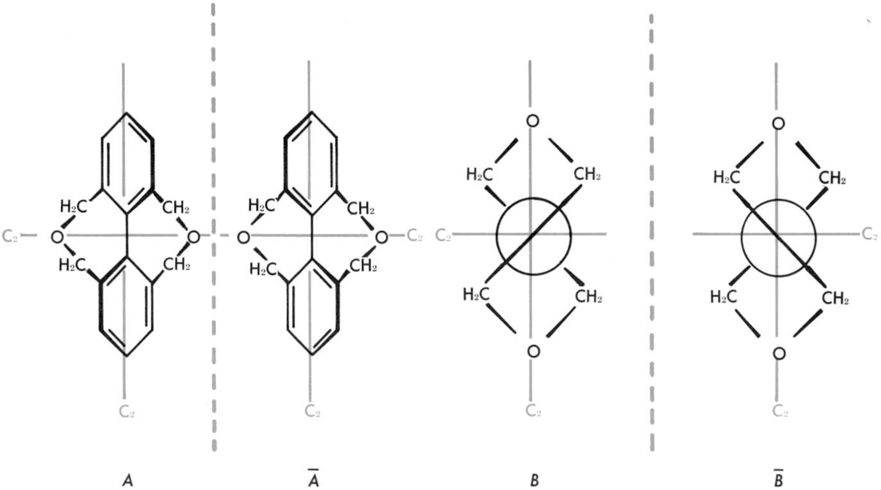

A Ā B B̄

FIGURE 1–16

D₂ *symmetry. In each drawing a third* C₂ *axis is perpendicular to the plane of the paper and intersects the other two* C₂ *axes in the center of the molecule.* A *and* Ā *are mirror images.* B *and* B̄ *are Newman projections of* A *and* Ā, *respectively. This point group is also called* **V**.

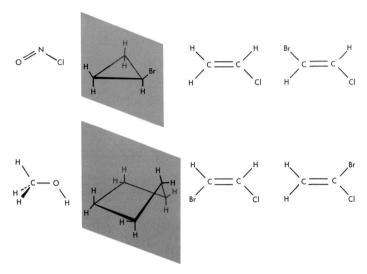

FIGURE 1–17

Examples of **C**$_s$. *Where necessary the* σ *plane is indicated* (*color*), *otherwise it is the plane of the paper. The molecule below bromocyclopropane is the "envelope" conformation of cyclopentane.*

ric molecule has a σ but no C_n, the group is **C**$_s$. We have encountered several examples (nitrosyl chloride (Figure 1–2*A*), bromocyclopropane, vinyl chloride), and more may be added (Figure 1–17). Very rarely, nondissymmetric molecules have no σ planes; this group is called **S**$_n$, where *n* refers to the order of the alternating axis which passes through the molecule (*n* is an even number). Examples are given in Figure 1–18. The presence of a σ is therefore not a necessary condition for reflection symmetry.

Most nondissymmetric molecules, however, have both σ planes and C_n axes. If there is only one C_n and all the σ planes intersect at C_n, the group is **C**$_{nv}$ (*v* = vertical) and the planes are σ$_v$. Water is **C**$_{2v}$ and ammonia is **C**$_{3v}$ (Figure 1–2*B* and *C*); other examples may be adduced:

C$_{2v}$: formaldehyde, methylene chloride, 1,1-dichloroethene
C$_{3v}$: chloroform, eclipsed 1, 1, 1-trichloroethane, chloromethane
C$_{xv}$: chloroacetylene, hydrogen chloride

If there is only one C_n and no σ containing that axis, but instead one σ perpendicular to that axis, the group is **C**$_{nh}$ (*h* = hori-

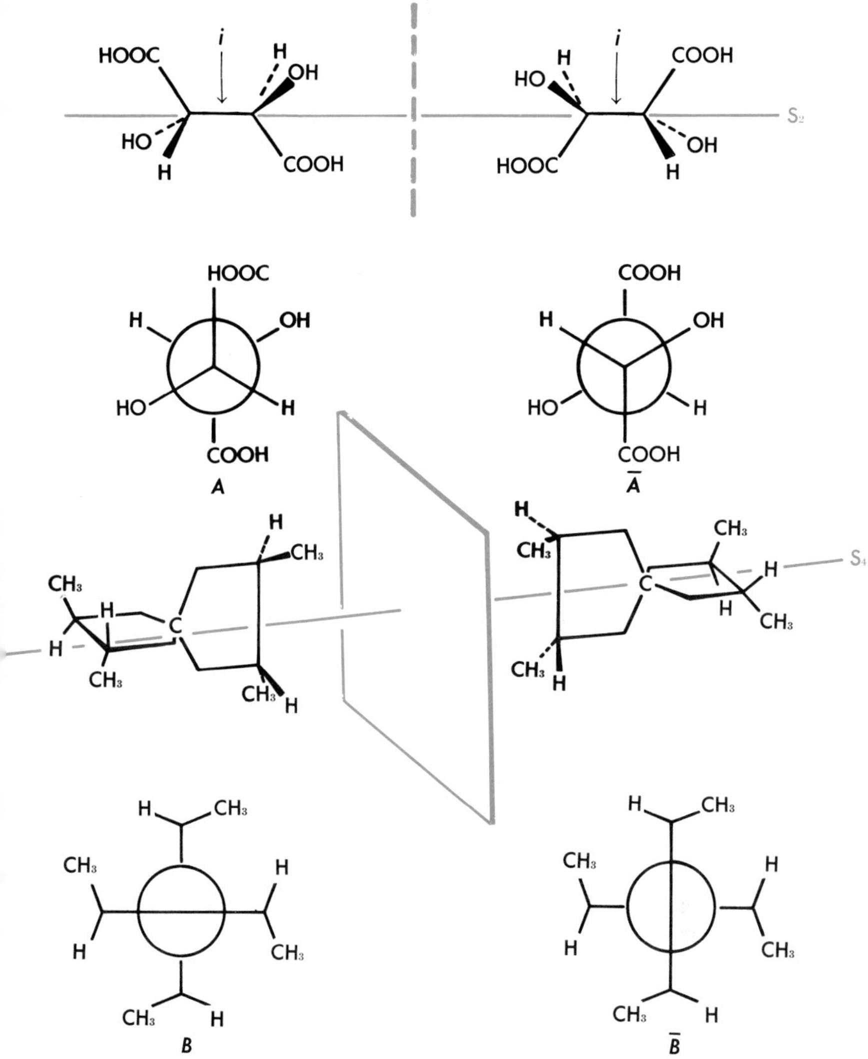

FIGURE 1–18

Examples of $\mathbf{S}_n$. Conformation A of meso-tartaric acid ($\mathbf{S}_2 \equiv \mathbf{C}_i$) has a S_2 axis ($\equiv$ center of symmetry i) as shown. After reflection in a mirror plane, A gives Ā which can be converted back into A by a 180° rotation around S_2. Spirane B ($\mathbf{S}_4$) has a S_4 axis coincident on a C_2 axis as shown. After reflection in a mirror plane, B gives B̄ which can be converted back into B by a 90° rotation around S_4. The Newman projections are shown below the perspective projections. Although the reflection plane properly passes through the center of the molecule, a mirror plane is shown to one side of the molecule for ease of representation.

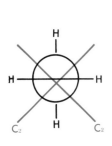 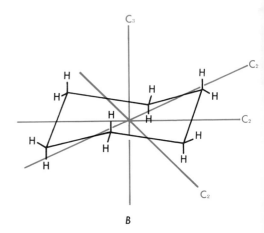

A B

FIGURE 1–19

Examples of $\mathbf{D}_{nd}$. *A, Newman projection of allene* ($\mathbf{D}_{2d}$ *or* $\mathbf{V}_d$); *the principal* C_2 *axis passes through the three carbon atoms and is perpendicular to the plane of the paper; the two σ-planes contain the H—C—H groupings. B, idealized chair cyclohexane* ($\mathbf{D}_{3d}$); *the three* σ *planes intersect at* C_3, *bisect the angles between the* C_2 *axes, and contain four hydrogen atoms each.*

zontal); the σ is σ_h. *Trans*-1,2-dichloroethene has $\mathbf{C}_{2h}$ symmetry.

Some nondissymmetric conformations have dihedral symmetry as well as n σ_v planes, but no σ_h ($\mathbf{D}_{nd}$, d = diagonal). The σ_v planes bisect the angles between the C_2 axes. An example is staggered ethane ($\mathbf{D}_{3d}$, Figure 1–10A), where the three σ_v planes contain H—C—C—H arrangements (such arrangements are called *trans* or *antiparallel* because the two C—H σ-bonds are parallel but point in opposite directions). Some other examples are given in Figure 1–19.

If dihedral symmetry is combined with n σ_v planes *plus* one σ_h which is perpendicular to the principal axis and contains the n C_2 axes, the group is $\mathbf{D}_{nh}$. Some examples follow:

$\mathbf{D}_{2h}$: ethylene, naphthalene.
$\mathbf{D}_{3h}$: eclipsed ethane (Figure 1–10B) methyl cation
      (Figure 1–4), cyclopropane (Figure 1–9).
$\mathbf{D}_{6h}$: benzene.
$\mathbf{D}_{\infty h}$: acetylene, carbon suboxide.

Summarizing:

Dissymmetric	*Nondissymmetric*
$\mathbf{C}_n = C_n$ only	$\mathbf{C}_s = \sigma$ only
$\mathbf{D}_n = C_n + n\,C_2$ only	$\mathbf{S}_n = $ no σ (n is even)
	$\mathbf{C}_{nv} = C_n + n\,\sigma_v$ only
	$\mathbf{C}_{nh} = C_n + \sigma_h$ only
	$\mathbf{D}_{nd} = C_n + n\,C_2 + n\,\sigma_v$ but no σ_h
	$\mathbf{D}_{nh} = C_n + n\,C_2 + n\,\sigma_v + \sigma_h$
	$\mathbf{T}_d = 4\,C_3 + 3\,C_2 + 6\,\sigma$ (Figure 1–6)
	$\mathbf{O}_h$: see exercise 1–17

The *symmetry number* (σ) is defined as the number of indistinguishable positions into which the molecule can be turned by simple rigid rotations. For $\mathbf{C}_s$ and $\mathbf{C}_i$ ($\equiv \mathbf{S}_2$), $\sigma = 1$. For $\mathbf{C}_n$, $\mathbf{C}_{nh}$ and $\mathbf{C}_{nv}$ ($n \neq \infty$) $\sigma = n$; for $\mathbf{C}_{\infty v}$, $\sigma = 1$. For $\mathbf{D}_n$, $\mathbf{D}_{nd}$ and $\mathbf{D}_{nh}$ ($n \neq \infty$), $\sigma = 2n$; for $\mathbf{D}_{\infty h}$, $\sigma = 2$. For $\mathbf{T}_d$, $\sigma = 12$, and for $\mathbf{O}_h$, $\sigma = 24$.

The student is now in a position to specify the point group of most conformations which he is likely to encounter in organic chemistry. He should be able to do the same for almost any physical object, and it is strongly recommended that he practice on these objects the knack of rapidly spotting symmetry elements and assigning the proper symmetry classification.

1–5   Molecular Deformations and Strain Energies

Thus far in our discussion we have considered the nuclei as stationary points in space, and only in the discussion of hydrogen molecule have we briefly referred to the actual vibration of the nuclei in the live molecule. In the present section we shall consider the problems encountered in the intramolecular motions of the nuclei, and the energy requirements associated with displacements of the nuclei from their equilibrium positions.

The change from a two-particle (i.e., H_2) to a three-particle system immensely complicates the description of molecular vibration, for in diatomic molecules bond length is the only variable, whereas in triatomic molecules *two* bond lengths *and* a bond angle must be considered as independent variables. For molecules more complex than triatomic systems, i.e., for most organic molecules, a correspondingly greater number of parameters must of course be considered. Despite this complexity, a discussion of the vibrating molecular system can be somewhat simplified by breaking down the intricate motions into three component types: bond stretching, bond bending, and bond torsion. These are collectively known as *molecular deformations.*

It must be stressed at the outset that such a distinction among types of deformations is artificial and purely a matter of convenience. Actually, the modes which we identify separately and by analogy with macroscopic models as bending, stretching, and torsion are felt collectively as changes in energy by the molecule as a whole.

Bond stretching and compression refers to the motion of bonded nuclei along the internuclear line. As in the analogous simple harmonic oscillator system of two masses connected by a spring, this vibration is governed by Hooke's quadratic law: The energy (V_r) required to distort the bond length (r) from its equilibrium position is proportional to the square of the linear displacement (Δr) (Eq. 1–6).

$$V_r = \tfrac{1}{2}k_r \, (\Delta r)^2 \qquad (1\text{--}6)$$

where k_r is the *bond stretching force constant.* The k_r values for C—H and C—C single bonds are about the same and are roughly one half the k_r values for C—C double bonds. One may thus write (Eqs. 1–7, 1–8):

$$\textit{For single bonds} \qquad\qquad (1\text{--}7)$$
$$V_r \sim 350 \, (\Delta r)^2 \; \text{kcal}/\text{mole}/\mathring{A}^2$$

$$\textit{For double bonds} \qquad\qquad (1\text{--}8)$$
$$V_r \sim 700 \, (\Delta r)^2 \; \text{kcal}/\text{mole}/\mathring{A}^2$$

This means that the linear deformation (stretching *or* compressing) of a single bond by as little as 0.03 Å requires the expenditure of 0.3 kcal/mole, and twice that for the stiffer double bond.

Bond angle bending refers to the radial scissoring motion of the bond angle, and this vibration is also governed by a Hooke's law relationship (Eq. 1–9).

$$V_\theta = \tfrac{1}{2}k_\theta \, (\Delta\theta)^2 \qquad (1\text{–}9)$$

where $\Delta\theta$ is the angular displacement from an equilibrium value, k_θ the *bond bending force constant,* and V_θ is the *angle strain* (or *Baeyer Strain*). The bending constant has very similar values for a wide variety of carbon bond angles encountered in organic molecules, and the energy relationship may in general be approximated (for deformations up to 20°) by an empirical equation (Eq. 1–10).

$$V_\theta \sim 0.01 \, (\Delta\theta)^2 \text{ kcal}/\text{mole}/\text{deg.}^2 \qquad (1\text{–}10)$$

This means that the energy requirement for the angular deformation of a C—C—C bond angle by 1° is only 0.01 kcal/mole; even an angular displacement of as much as 10° requires no more energy (1 kcal/mole) than is needed to perform a linear displacement of 0.05 Å along a single bond axis. Bond angles are therefore easily deformed. The reference point for angle deformations, i.e., the geometry corresponding to $V_\theta = 0$, is properly that of the presumably unstrained acyclic species, e.g. 112° for C—CH$_2$—C bond angles. It must also be noted that $\Delta\theta$ in the above expression refers to the *internuclear* angle. For small angular displacements this is essentially identical with the interorbital angle. However, the more the internuclear angle is deformed (given the same coordination number), the greater becomes the discrepancy between the internuclear and the interorbital angle, in the sense that the latter lags behind the former. At the same time the bond bending force constant decreases, so that the energy requirement per degree of angle bending progressively decreases as the angle is deformed more and more. As a result the energy of bending the tetrahedral angle to the cyclopropane 60° angle is much less than calculated by the above equation.

Bond torsion refers to the rotational motion around the bond axis. The energy relationship in its simplest form may be written as (Eq. 1–11):

$$V_\phi = \tfrac{1}{2}V_0 \, (1 + \cos n\Delta\phi) \text{ kcal}/\text{mole} \qquad (1\text{–}11)$$

where $\Delta\phi$ is the displacement of the dihedral angle, V_0 is the *torsional energy barrier,* n is the *periodicity* (i.e., the number of times that a given conformation recurs in a complete revolution; $\Delta\phi = 360°$), and V_ϕ is the *torsional strain* (or *Pitzer strain*). The equation is directly applicable in the above form to molecules which have a periodicity greater than unity, for example ethane ($n = 3$). The change of V_ϕ with $\Delta\phi$ is shown graphically in Figure 1–20. The energy required to go from a minimum to a maximum is the *n*-fold *torsional energy barrier* (activation energy). In the present example this is only about 3 kcal/mole. Thus rotation around the C—C single bond, though not free, is certainly quite facile. In general, the greater the periodicity, the smaller the barrier. Thus nitromethane, with $n = 6$, has a torsional barrier of only 0.006 kcal/mole.

The conformation at the top of the torsional energy barrier in ethane is eclipsed, the conformation at the bottom of the energy

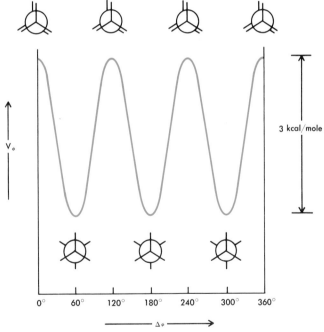

FIGURE 1–20

Torsional strain (V_ϕ) as a function of angular displacement ($\Delta\phi$) in ethane.

well (the *equilibrium conformation*) is staggered, and all other conformations are dissymmetrically skewed (Figure 1–10).

It is useful to think of torsion around the σ-bond axis of a double bond in similar terms. Although the origin of the torsional barrier in ethane is not fully understood, the magnitude of the torsional barrier in olefins (about 60 kcal/mole) may be ascribed to the necessity of breaking a π-bond (hence, *restricted rotation*).

The relationship between V_ϕ and $\Delta\phi$ becomes more complex when the periodicity is unity, i.e., when a given conformation does not recur within a complete torsional revolution. This is the case with molecules of type A—CX_2—CX_2—B, with A = B (e.g., butane, where A = B = CH_3 and X = H) or with A $\neq$ B (e.g., *n*-propyl chloride, where A = CH_3, B = Cl, and X = H). The change of V_ϕ with $\Delta\phi$ is schematically indicated in Figure 1–21. The equilibrium conformation at $\Delta\phi = 180°$ is called *anti* and the skew equilibrium conformations near $\Delta\phi = 60°$ and $300°$ are

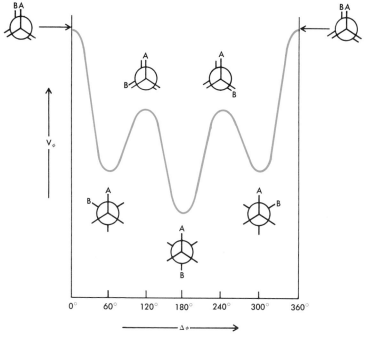

FIGURE 1–21

Torsional strain (V_ϕ) *as a function of angular displacement* ($\Delta\phi$) *in molecules of type* A—CX_2—CX_2—B.

called *gauche*. Although the diagram in Figure 1–21 implies that *gauche* conformations are less stable than *anti*-conformations, this is in fact not always the case. In butane, and in 1,2,-dibromoethane, the *anti*-conformation is indeed more stable than the *gauche* by 0.8 kcal/mole. However, in 1,2-dichloroethane, and in *n*-propyl chloride, the *anti* and the *gauche* conformations have approximately the same energy. Finally, in 1,1,2,2-tetrachloro- and in 1,1,2,2-tetrabromoethane (A = B = H, X = halogen), the *anti* conformation is *less* stable than the *gauche* form by 1.0 kcal/mole.

An entirely analogous situation exists in olefins of type A—CX=CX—B, with A = B (e.g., 2-butene, where A = B = CH_3 and X=H) or with A ≠ B (e.g., 1-chloropropene, where A = CH_3, B = Cl, and X=H). The change of V_ϕ with $\Delta\phi$ is schematically indicated in Figure 1–22. The equilibrium conformation at $\Delta\phi = 90°$ is the *cis*-conformation and the equilibrium conformation at $\Delta\phi = 270°$ the *trans*-conformation. Although the diagram in Figure 1–22 implies that *trans*-conformations are more stable than *cis*-conformations, this is not always the case. Thus, whereas *trans*-2,2,5,5-tetramethyl-3-hexene is more stable than the *cis*-form by 9 kcal/mole and *trans*-2-butene is more stable than the *cis*-form by 1 kcal/mole, *trans*-1,2-dichloroethene on the other hand is *less* stable than the *cis*-form by 0.5 kcal/mole. In fact, of the ten possible 1,2-dihaloethenes, only one (the diiodo compound) exists preferentially in the *trans*-form.

It is not possible in all cases (notably with halogen-containing compounds) to account fully for the observed differences in stability. However, there can be no doubt that in the large majority of instances (especially hydrocarbons) the differences in stability arise to an important extent from differences in nonbonded interactions between the substituents on the neighboring carbon atoms.

Inter- and intramolecular nonbonded interactions are of great importance in stereochemistry: structure and reactivity depend to a large extent on this factor from which virtually all *steric effects* arise; indeed, the terms "steric" and "nonbonded" are on many occasions used synonymously.

Nonbonded interactions depend on the internuclear distance (ρ) between nonbonded atoms and are expressed in potential functions ($V\rho$). These are the sums of attractive terms ($V_A = -A/\rho^6$) and repulsive terms ($V_B = B/\rho^{12}$ or $Be^{-\mu\rho}$), where A and B are con-

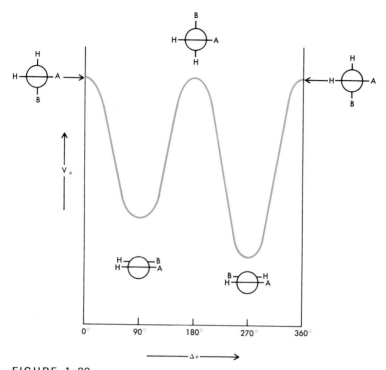

FIGURE 1-22

Torsional strain as a function of angular displacement ($\Delta\phi$) in molecules of type A—CH=CH—B.

stants which depend on the nature of the interacting atoms. As illustrated in Figure 1-23 for a typical interaction potential (carbon-carbon), V_B, which is always positive, rises steeply at small internuclear distances and falls off rapidly at larger distances, whereas the curvature of V_A is less extreme and of opposite sign. In consequence, the net potential V_ρ is slightly negative (attractive) at all distances above 2.8 Å but becomes strongly positive (repulsive) at distances below 2.8 Å. It is for this reason that repulsive terms are generally considered the most important factors in nonbonded interactions at small internuclear distances. The shallow minimum corresponds to the equilibrium distance of the nonbonded atoms.

The total molecular strain energy (V_T) is the sum of all the individual terms (Eq. 1-12).

$$V_T = V_r(r) + V_\theta\,(\theta) + V_\phi\,(\phi) + V_\rho\,(\rho) \qquad (1\text{--}12)$$

V_T is therefore a function of the geometrical parameters r, θ, ϕ, and ρ which define the molecular conformation. Since the molecule seeks to achieve the level of lowest potential energy, the equilibrium values of r, θ, ϕ, and ρ are those corresponding to the minimum value of V_T ($= V_{min}$). If the functions $V_\theta\,(r)$, $V_\theta\,(\theta)$, $V_\phi\,(\phi)$, and $V_\rho\,(\rho)$ are accurately known, V_{min} may therefore be computed and the values of r, θ, ϕ, and ρ corresponding to V_{min} may thus be estimated. In other words: From a knowledge of the

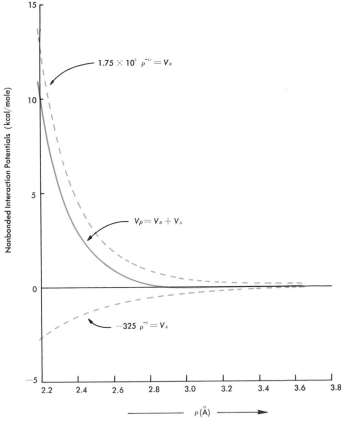

FIGURE 1–23

Nonbonded interaction (V_ρ) as a function of internuclear distance (ρ). The example refers to a C/C interaction.

dependence of strain energy on geometry, it is in principle possible to arrive at a description of the molecular conformation under consideration. Unfortunately the accent is on the provisional "in principle," for although the mathematical apparatus for performing the required computations is more than adequate, the same cannot often be said of the functions describing the dependence of energy on geometry. These functions are approximate at best, and often the choice of a particular function becomes a matter of arbitrary judgment. Nevertheless, despite these obvious shortcomings, the energy relationships discussed above are still useful for obtaining at least crude estimates of molecular geometry, and for accounting qualitatively and within an order of magnitude for the conformations and for the conformational changes which are observed by physical and chemical methods.

The conformation corresponding to V_{min} is the equilibrium conformation. The stretching vibrations (Δr), the in-plane angle bending vibrations ($\Delta \theta$), and the torsional oscillations (librations, $\Delta \phi$) about the equilibrium positions r, θ, and ϕ, respectively, are governed by V_T, and the magnitudes of the individual deformations are dictated by the partitioning of V_T among the component energy terms. Thus, the soft bond angles will generally perform large scissoring motions whereas the stiff bond lengths will be less extensively deformed.

In the preceding discussions, the electronic ground state has been tacitly assumed, and we shall continue to base our subsequent discussions on this assumption. It must be kept in mind, however, that the distribution of electrons in an electronically excited state is different from that in the ground state. If this excited state persists for a long enough period of time, the nuclei will redistribute themselves by vibrational relaxation to new equilibrium positions, corresponding to a new value of V_{min}. Structure in the present stereochemical context therefore depends on the electronic state. For example, acetylene in the ground state is a linear ($\mathbf{D}_{\infty h}$) molecule with C—H and C—C bond distances of 1.06 and 1.20 Å, respectively, whereas in the ^1A_u excited state it is *trans*-bent ($\mathbf{C}_{2h}$), with < CCH 120°, C—H 1.08 Å, and C—C 1.39 Å. Similarly, formaldehyde in the ground state is planar ($\mathbf{C}_{2v}$), with < HCH 118°, C—H 1.12 Å and CO 1.21 Å, whereas in the first excited state it is bent ($\mathbf{C}_s$), with < HCH 122°, C—H 1.09 Å, C—O 1.32 Å, and a 20° angle between the C—O internuclear line and the H—C—H plane.

1–6   Molecular Models

In the preceding sections we have learned to describe the structure and topology of simple organic molecules. In detailed discussions of complex molecules, however, a complete description becomes forbiddingly involved. It is therefore customary to resort to a short cut by using a highly simplified symbolism: molecular models.

The well-known usefulness of models lies in the immediate recognition, merely by processes of manipulation, inspection, and (with scaled models) mensuration, of the spatial relationship between atoms in various conformations of a molecule. In addition it is possible to study, again just by inspection, the topology of interaction between different molecules. However, it cannot be overemphasized that a model at best merely *abstracts* a few particular and selected molecular properties, and there is always considerable loss of information in the abstraction. This difficulty is compounded by the circumstance that commercially available model sets are in fact collections of *atomic* models. These kits are designed to permit the construction of many molecular models from a limited number of atomic parts, and for most purposes this necessary oversimplification does not introduce a serious error. Nevertheless, the intelligent use of molecular models requires an awareness of these oversimplifications.

All available model sets have only one kind of tetracoordinate carbon atom. In this atomic model the bond attachments (valences) are arranged in the symmetry of a regular tetrahedron, i.e., all bond angles are set at 109.5°. Let us now construct a model of a molecule *Cabcd* in which all four ligand atoms are different. We recognize by inspection the absence of reflection symmetry, i.e., we can distinguish, by comparison, the object and its mirror image. We may also identify the configuration. We *cannot,* however, see the differences in the six bond angles; we only know that these differences must exist and that we must therefore read them into the model if we are to arrive at a more complete description of the molecule. In other words, the model summarizes and emphasizes some aspects of the molecular properties and completely suppresses, in fact falsifies, others. This example may be extended to all those cases in which the model of the central atom has been constructed with fixed and regular bonding angles (e.g., all carbonyl carbons, which are constructed with 120° angles). Our point is that many bond angles are not realistically reflected in molecular models made from sets.

In a closely related oversimplification, the hybridization indices of σ-bonded carbon atoms are usually given as 3, 2, or 1, depending on the coordination number (4, 3, and 2, respectively), regardless of the equivalence or nonequivalence of ligands. By and large this approximation is not too far off the mark—for example when reference is made to sp^3 carbon in methyl fluoride and to sp^2 carbon in formaldehyde or ethylene. Sometimes, however, a designation of an "average" hybridization may be deceiving. Thus, in acetyl chloride, the three orbitals are approximately $sp^{3.2}$, $sp^{1.0}$ and $sp^{2.6}$; it is misleading to refer to the central carbon as sp^2. In just the same way the molecular model of acetyl chloride, which is built from a trigonal carbonyl carbon atom whose valence angles are set at 120°, gives the incorrect molecular geometry.

Bond distances on the other hand are usually quite reliable because of the curious circumstance that bond lengths are given fairly accurately by the sums of "atomic radii" which are assigned to each bonding atom. These atomic radii are built into the atomic models from which the molecular models are constructed.

Another serious problem arises from the fact that molecular models often do not give an adequate picture of internuclear motion. Stiffness in the bond lengths is reasonable, but stiffness in the bond angles is not. As to torsional motion, molecular models give the feeling of free rotation around single bonds and essentially completely restricted rotation around double bonds, neither of which, as we have learned, corresponds to the actual behavior.

Some "space-filling" models indicate regions of high electron density by use of material which is shaped in a scaled replica of the outer contour surface (i.e., the one containing 90% to 95% of the electron) of the bonding and nonbonding orbitals. Such models permit some estimate of the nearness of regions of high electron density in various geometric arrangements and hence allow a crude guess at the importance of nonbonded interactions (steric effects) in various situations. The spatial position of the nuclei is virtually impossible to gauge in such models. In contrast, other types of molecular models emphasize the relative positions of nuclei in space by leaving out entirely any representations of electron density. The two types of models, the former illustrated by the Stuart-

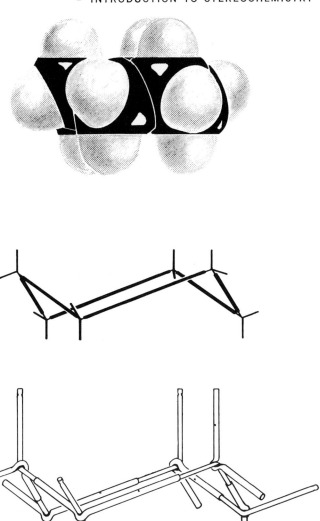

FIGURE 1–24

Representation of some types of molecular models of cyclohexane (left) and benzene (right.) Top: space-filling Stuart-Briegleb models. Center: Brumlik "Framework Molecular Orbital" models, showing the σ- and π-lattices. Bottom: Dreiding models, which show the σ-framework.

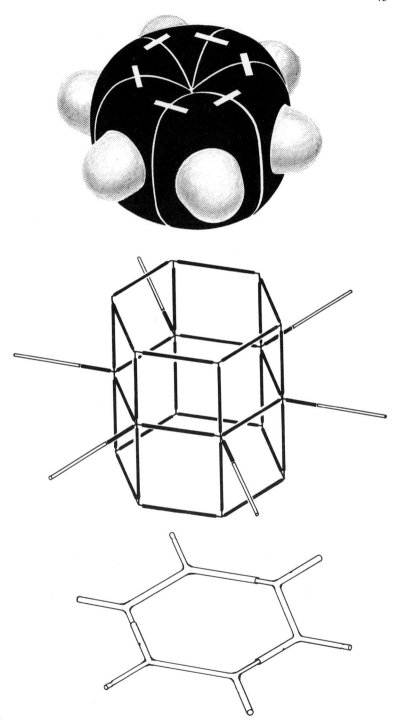

Briegleb models and the latter by the Dreiding or Brumlik models, abstract very different aspects of the structure, and neither of them is therefore more than a partial and limited representation of the same molecule (Figure 1–24). It is a question of judgment which molecular model should be consulted, for the answer to that question depends on the kind of information that is required. Whichever model or combination of models is chosen, the student must in his imagination supply the many missing shades and subtleties.

Finally, but most importantly, molecular models are built to reflect the behavior of an "average" molecule near room temperature and are completely insensitive to the changes in the properties of molecular aggregates which result from changes in temperature. As the temperature is increased, the population of molecules with a high energy content increases at the expense of those with lower energy content. Thus at high temperatures the bulk properties of the compound reflect more nearly the behavior of the "hot" molecule which undergoes molecular deformations and other changes with greater ease than that of the "cold" molecule at lower temperatures. For example, what appears to be "restricted" rotation (torsion) at room temperature may become virtually "free" rotation at elevated temperatures, and similarly "free" rotation at room temperature may become "restricted" rotation at very low temperatures! This important limitation of models finds its most vivid expression in problems associated with torsional isomerism (section 2–4).

1–7   Exercises

1–1   Calculate the C—C—C interorbital angles and carbon hybridizations for the bent bond description of acetylene. Assume two $2sp_x$–$1s$ C—H bonds and (a) three bent bonds, (b) two bent bonds and a π_z-bond.

1–2   (a) Account for the bonding geometry in allene and cumulene by using the bent bond rather than the σ,π description. Assume sp^3 for the central carbon AO's.

(b) Discuss qualitatively the hybridization of the central carbon atom in spiropentane.

1–3   It is frequently noted that ring closure occurs more readily with compounds of the type $(CH_3)_2C[(CH_2)_nX]_2$ than with compounds of the type $CH_2[(CH_2)_nX]_2$ (the gem-dimethyl effect). Account qualitatively for this effect.

1-4   Ferrocene, $(C_5H_5)_2$ Fe, consists of an iron atom sandwiched between two parallel C_5H_5 plates, each of which in isolation is a ring with D_{5h} symmetry. Torsion takes place readily (i.e., about as easily as in ethane) about an axis which is the common C_5 axis of the two C_5H_5 rings and which passes through the iron atom. What are the symmetries of the eclipsed, staggered, and skewed conformations of ferrocene? Are the last named dissymmetric? Asymmetric? What is the periodicity of the torsional motion?

1-5   Two conformations of cyclobutane, the planar (D_{4h}) and the diagonally folded (D_{2d}), are shown below. Identify the symmetry elements.

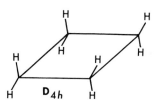
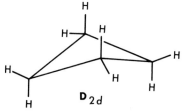

(a) What are the symmetry classifications (point groups) of 1-fluoro-cyclobutane, 1,1-difluorocyclobutane, and 1,1,3,3-tetrafluorocyclo-butane given either one of the above geometries?

(b) Estimate the angle strain in the D_{4h} conformation of cyclobutane.

1-6   The acid strength of hydrocarbons decreases with decreasing s-character of the bonding carbon AO, i.e., acetylene > ethylene > ethane. What is the effect of ring-size on the acid strengths of cycloalkanes?

1-7   (a) Show that $S_1 \equiv \sigma$ and that $S_2 \equiv i$ (center of symmetry)

(b) Show that $C_{1v} \equiv C_{1h} \equiv C_s$

(c) Show that cylindrical symmetry $\equiv D_{\infty h}$, and conical symmetry $\equiv C_{\infty v}$.

1-8   What are the symmetry classifications (point groups) of norbornane (I), bicyclo[2.2.2]octane (II), twistane (III), and adamantane (IV)? Using symmetry arguments only, how many different C—C bond lengths and C—C—C bond angles are there in each of these compounds?

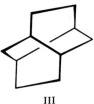
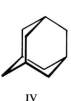

I   II   III   IV

1-9   The position of the carbonyl absorption band of ketones in the infrared spectrum is a sensitive measure of θ, the C—CO—C bond angle: $\theta = (1974 - \nu)/2.2$, where ν gives the position of the maximum in cm^{-1}. Thus acetone and cyclohexanone, with ν 1718, have $\theta = 116°$. Using acetone and cyclohexanone as strain-free standards in the acyclic and cyclic series of ketones, respectively, compute bond angles and carbonyl bond angle strain energies in the following two series of compounds and qualitatively account for the results:

(a) Methyl t-butyl ketone (ν1710), t-butyl t-amyl ketone (ν1684)

(b) Cyclobutanone (ν1792), cyclopentanone (ν1750), cycloheptanone (ν1705)

1-10   Consider torsional motions about the C_{sp3}—C_{sp2} bond axis of toluene.

(a) Give a conformational analysis; indicate point groups.

(b) Assuming that the equilibrium conformation is eclipsed C_s and that the staggered C_s conformation corresponds to an energy maximum, give the periodicity of the torsional motion. Would your answer have been different if the energy relationships had been reversed?

1-11   (a) If the nonbonded potential is of the form $V_\rho = B/\rho^{12} - A/\rho^6$, show that the equilibrium distance ρ_{min} is given by $\sqrt[6]{2B/A}$. For the function shown in Figure 1-23, calculate ρ_{min} and V_{min}.

(b) Plot V_A, V_R, and V_ρ for the nonbonded function corresponding to the interaction of two nonbonded hydrogen atoms: $V_\rho = 1.36 \times 10^4\, e^{-4.72\rho} - 49.2/\rho^6$ kcal/mole (ρ in Å units) and find ρ_{min}.

1-12   The aromatic compound 1,8-bisdehydro[14]annulene has D_{2h} symmetry. A valence bond representation is shown below. One of the criteria of aromaticity is met by the presence of a π-framework containing 14 benzenoid electrons. Describe the bonding in this molecule (σ- and π-lattice).

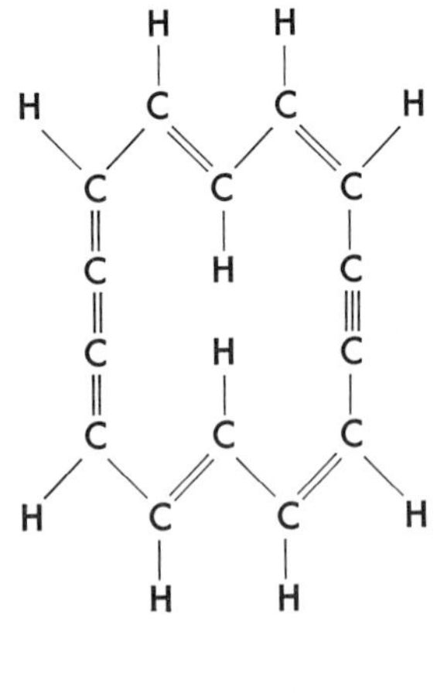

1–13 (a) What molecular symmetries (give point groups) are a sufficient condition for the absence of a torsional barrier?

(b) Is this a necessary condition?

1–14 (a) Estimate J_{CH} for methane, ethylene and methylacetylene (the acetylenic carbon).

(b) Given J_{CH} for cyclopropane (161 cps), cyclobutane (134 cps), cubane (160 cps), cyclopentane (128 cps), cyclohexane (124 cps), and cyclodecane (118 cps), estimate the C—C—C interorbital angles in these compounds.

1–15 Give the possible symmetries for the following four objects and consider all of the possible permutations: (a) a flat cardboard square, through the four corners of which 4 nails have been perpendicularly driven; (b) ditto, with 4 right-handed screws replacing the nails; (c) ditto, but 3 right-handed and one left-handed screw; (d) ditto, but two right-handed and two left-handed screws.

1–16 If an atom of a nontransition element A is bonded to n ligands X and has m lone electron pairs E, the general shape of the molecule AX_nE_m is given by $i = n + m$ and is a consequence of the repulsive interactions between bonding and nonbonding pairs. Specifically, for A = carbon, nitrogen or oxygen, the shape is tetrahedral for $i = 4$, trigonal $i = 3$, and linear for $i = 2$. Show how this generalization holds for the examples studied in this chapter and also for the following molecules: methyl anion and cation, nitrate ion ($\mathbf{D}_{3h}$), nitrite ion ($\mathbf{C}_{2v}$), nitronium ion ($\mathbf{D}_{\infty h}$).

1–17 The point group $\mathbf{O}_h$ is exemplified by cubane (C_8H_8), which has the symmetry of a cube. List the symmetry elements (C_n and σ only).

1–18 True or false?

(a) Dissymmetry is a necessary and sufficient condition for asymmetry.

(b) A nondissymmetric conformation with a C_n must also have a σ.

(c) A nondissymmetric conformation with a σ must also have a C_n.

(d) All dissymmetric conformations have a S_n.

(e) Absence of a σ is a necessary but not a sufficient condition for dissymmetry.

(f) Presence of a σ is a sufficient but not a necessary condition for reflection symmetry.

2

STEREOISOMERISM ▪

2–1   Classification of Structural Isomerism
Enantiomeric and Diastereomeric Relationships

Isomers, or *structural isomers,* are defined as chemical species which have the same molecular formula but differ in structure and are separated by energy barriers. It is this last restriction which differentiates "structural isomers" from "conformations": Many conformations are possible for a single isomer. Since the concept of isomers is a practical one only as long as the isomers do not interconvert at immeasurably fast rates, it is useful to make the above definition more operational by adding the following restrictions: The measurement which distinguishes the isomers must be rapid compared to the rate of interconversion (the latter depends on the height of the energy barrier and on the temperature). This definition is completely independent of the nature of the barrier, i.e., of the transition state for interconversion.

In order to classify structural isomers further, we shall distinguish between *constitutional isomers* (called structural isomers in some texts) and *stereoisomers.*

The constitution of a molecule is a description of the sequential arrangement of atoms regardless of direction in space. Word pictures of partial bonding arrangements are sufficient to discriminate between particular constitutional isomers. Thus "the isomer of C_4H_{10} which contains one carbon atom attached to three others" suffices to identify isobutane as distinct from *n*-butane; note that the "attachment" refers to the *nearest* neighbors. Similarly, the statement that "in a molecule C_4H_9D, the carbon which is attached to the deuterium is also attached to a single protium" unequivocally singles out and identifies one ($CH_3CH_2CHDCH_3$) among four constitutional isomers.

Stereoisomerism arises because molecules which have the same constitution may still differ, as isomers, in the spatial arrangements of their atoms. There are several possible ways in which stereoisomers may be classified, and such classifications may be made at two entirely distinct and separate levels. In the *symmetry classification* the only characteristics which distinguish the isomers are their symmetry properties. The other type of classification depends only on those structural features which are related to the nature and magnitude of the energy barrier separating the isomers (*barrier classification*). These two independent points of view are complementary rather than mutually exclusive.

The symmetry classification of stereoisomers rests on an exceedingly simple criterion: Either the isomers are related as object and mirror image, or they are not. Stereoisomers which are related as object and nonsuperimposable mirror image are called *enantiomers* or *antipodes,* whereas those which are not so related are called *diastereomers.* Two stereoisomers cannot be at the same time both enantiomers and diastereomers of each other. A molecule (or object) may have only one enantiomer but, structural conditions permitting, a molecule may have many diastereomers. In the following discussions the term *enantiomeric* will be applied to any relationship which is that of an object and its nonsuperimposable mirror image whereas the term *diastereomeric* will be applied to any spatial relationship which is not an enantiomeric one.

In order to exist in enantiomeric forms, it is necessary that the molecule be dissymmetric. It follows that only molecules with symmetry C_n or D_n may exist in enantiomeric forms.

The relationship between enantiomers simply resembles the relationship between right- and left-handed helices. The screw sense (right or left) which characterizes a given dissymmetric conformation or helix is the *chirality,* a term which may be applied to any dissymmetric object or molecule and which refers to the handedness of a given enantiomeric form. Obviously only two chiralities are possible for any one conformation.

It must now be pointed out that *chirality cannot be specified without comparison with a standard which is itself dissymmetric.* Thus, the concept "right-handed" cannot be communicated without using arbitrary expressions like "clockwise," which depend on common visual experience and common agreement on direction. Another way of saying this is that we have no obvious way of deciding whether we live in a given universe or in a world which is the mirror image of that universe. The term "right-handed" therefore has no meaning apart from the common agreement on what constitutes right-handedness, and every time that it is desired to designate the chirality of a conformation, it becomes necessary anew to make a comparison, implicitly or explicitly, between the conformation whose chirality is to be specified and a dissymmetric standard—a handle, as it were—of defined chirality. This point is illustrated in the manual separation of *enantiomorphous crystals,* i.e., crystals with mirror-image habits.

Figure 2–1 shows the enantiomorphous forms of quartz and of sodium ammonium tartrate; both crystals are hemihedral, i.e., they have facets which in combination form a dissymmetric habit. In 1848, Pasteur manually separated the crystals of sodium ammonium tartrate into two groups of crystals which differed according to the chirality of their crystal habit, an experiment which proved to be epoch-making and to which we shall return in sections 2.2 and 3.1. Our point here is that this manual separation was made possible only by a visual comparison of each individual crystal with a dissymmetric standard, i.e., with a previously segregated crystal, and by making each time anew the decision "the new crystal and the standard crystal are alike—i.e., they have the same dissymmetric habit" or "the new crystal and the standard crystal are not alike—i.e., they have enantiomorphous habits," whichever happened to be the case.

The preceding illustration now leads us to a principle which is basic to all of stereochemistry. Let us place two hemihedral crystals of identical appearance into juxtaposition (pair A). Now let us place two hemihedral crystals of enantiomorphous habit into juxtaposition (pair B). The relationship between pair A and pair

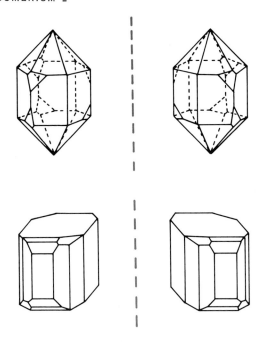

FIGURE 2–1

Enantiomorphous crystals. Top, hemihedral quartz; bottom, sodium ammonium tartrate.

B is no longer the relationship between an object and its mirror image. Rather, the relationship is that between two conspicuously different objects (taking each pair as a single object) *which may be descriptively distinguished without recourse to a dissymmetric standard.* Since the relationship between pair A and pair B is purely spatial, and since the relationship is nonenantiomeric, it is by our definition diastereomeric. In general: *A distinction between enantiomers may be achieved solely on the basis of a difference in diastereomeric interactions or relationships. Conversely, the very existence of such diastereomeric interactions or relationship is not only a necessary but in principle also a sufficient condition for the distinction between enantiomers.* This fundamental principle of stereochemistry is again illustrated in Figure 2–2 for the case of a helix.

The operational distinctions between enantiomers by physical methods, the methods used to separate them, and any differences in

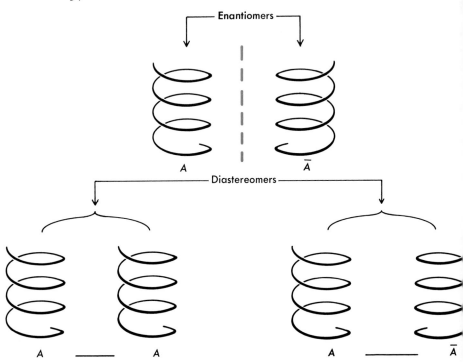

FIGURE 2–2

Schematization of the basic symmetry relationships of stereoisomers. Enantiomeric helices of opposite chirality are shown above (A and Ā). Combination of A with itself (lower left) and with Ā (lower right) creates two diastereomeric objects. The interactions A-A and A-Ā differ visibly and dramatically, as can be seen by nestling two mirror-image helices (A-Ā) and then attempting to do the same with two helices which are identical (A-A): They just won't fit! A is defined as a left-handed and Ā as a right-handed helix.

reactivity, including the oft-encountered differences in biological activity, are all consequences of this principle. We shall return to this point in subsequent discussions.

2–2   Optical Activity

The most conspicuous physical property of dissymmetric substances is their *optical activity* or *optical rotatory power,* specifically: their ability to refract and absorb right and left circularly polarized light to different extents.

A beam of light has associated with it time-dependent electric and magnetic fields. The behavior of the electric field may be indicated by vector **E** whose magnitude and direction are those of the sinusoidally oscillating field. If the oscillation occurs in, say, the xz plane for a wave traveling in the z-direction, the light is *plane-polarized* (Figure 2–3). As indicated in Figure 2–4, plane-polarized light may be considered the resultant of two circularly

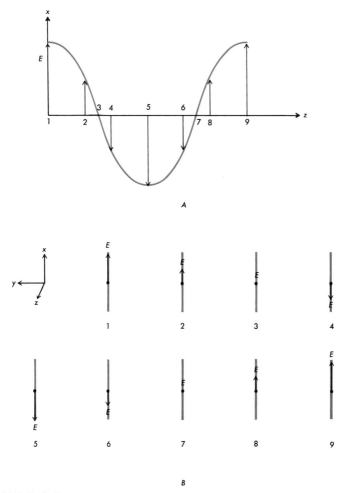

FIGURE 2–3

Plane-polarized light. **A,** *motion of the electric field vector in the* z-*direction.* **B,** *same oscillation projected on the xy-plane.*

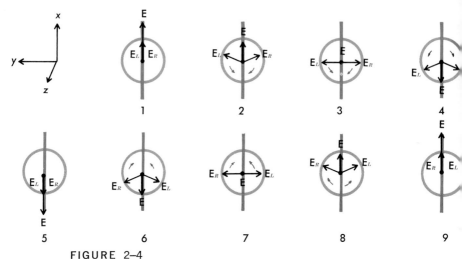

FIGURE 2–4

*Projection on the xy-plane of the electric field vector **E** of plane-polarized light (Figure 2–3), shown as the resultant of two in-phase beams of right and left circularly polarized light, $\mathbf{E_R}$ and $\mathbf{E_L}$. $\mathbf{E_R}$ traces out a right-handed helix (clockwise and away from the observer in the z-direction) whose pitch is λ, and whose amplitude is one half the amplitude of **E**. $\mathbf{E_L}$ traces out the corresponding left-handed helix.*

polarized in-phase beams of the same frequency and half the amplitude of vibration. The electric vectors associated with each of the two beams, $\mathbf{E_R}$ (R = right) and $\mathbf{E_L}$ (L = left), trace out helical paths of opposite chiralities so that circularly polarized light is dissymmetric. In a dissymmetric medium the condition necessary for the distinction between mirror images is therefore satisfied: A diastereomeric relationship exists between right circularly polarized light passing through a dissymmetric medium of given chirality, and left circularly polarized light passing through the identical medium. It follows that a dissymmetric medium is capable of distinguishing between the two beams of opposite chirality. The distinction takes the form of differences in refractive indices of the two beams ($n_R \neq n_L$) and differences in molar extinction coefficients ($\epsilon_R \neq \epsilon_L$). The former is called *circular birefringence* and the latter *circular dichroism*.

Dissymmetric media may consist of a collection of nondissymmetric particles rigidly locked in a dissymmetric array, as within a crystal lattice. Thus, a crystal of quartz (Figure 2–1) may be regarded as a giant dissymmetric SiO_2 polymer molecule prevented by lattice forces from losing its chirality. For the organic chemist the more important media are those which consist of collections of relatively small dissymmetric molecules in the liquid state.

CIRCULAR BIREFRINGENCE   The difference in refractive indices n_R and n_L of two circularly polarized beams of light in a dissymmetric medium corresponds to the slowing of one beam relative to the other. This has the consequence of continuously rotating the plane of polarization (*optical rotation*) as indicated in Figure 2–5; the plane of polarization is thus changed into a figure resembling a twisted ribbon during the passage of light through the dissymmetric medium. The angle of rotation (α) in degrees per centimeter is given by Eq. 2–1.

$$\alpha = \frac{180}{\lambda}(n_L - n_R) \qquad (2\text{–}1)$$

For example, if an observed optical rotation at 360 mμ is 1° and the path length is 10 cm. (= 1 dm.), then $n_L - n_R = 2 \times 10^{-8}$. This is a tiny fraction of the absolute value, i.e., about one millionth of one per cent.

The magnitude of the measured angle of rotation for a given solute, solvent, wave length λ, and temperature T is proportional to the number of molecules in the path of the light, i.e., to the product of the path length and the concentration or density; this is *Biot's law*. The proportionality constant is the *specific rotation*, [α], or the *molecular rotation*, [ϕ], depending on the units of con-

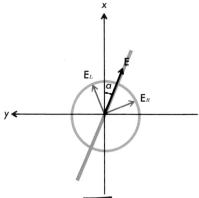

FIGURE 2–5

Change in the direction of the plane of polarized light(projection **E***) as the result of a change in the velocity of* **E**$_R$ *relative to* **E**$_L$.

centration. The specific rotation expresses the rotation (α, in degrees) of a sample per unit path length (l, in dm.) and concentration (c, in g/100 ml. of solution) for solutions, or density (d, in g/ml.) for pure liquids (i.e., "neat"); M = molecular weight (Eq. 2–2).

$$[\alpha]_\lambda^T = \frac{\alpha_\lambda^T \times 100}{l \times c}; \ [\alpha]_\lambda^T = \frac{\alpha_\lambda^T}{l \times d}; \ [\phi]_\lambda^T = \frac{M \ [\alpha]_\lambda^T}{100} \qquad (2\text{–}2)$$

$[\alpha]_\lambda^T$ and $[\phi]_\lambda^T$ are in principle constant and independent of l and c. However, any observed values of $\alpha \pm 180 \ n$ (n = 0,1,-2 . . .) are necessarily indistinguishable and it is advisable therefore to perform a measurement at two concentrations (or two path lengths). For example, an observed rotation at c and l of $+10°$ could equally well be $+190°$, $-170°$, etc. However, at 0.1 c and l, or at c and 0.1 l, $\alpha = +1°$ which is clearly distinguishable from $+19°$, $-17°$, etc. In another sense, $[\alpha]_\lambda^T$ and $[\phi]_\lambda^T$ are dependent on concentration when the molecular species enter into various association equilibria (as is particularly true with hydrogen-bonding solvents and solutes), since each species— monomer, dimer, etc.—has then its own value of $[\alpha]_\lambda^T$ and the *observed* $[\alpha]_\lambda^T$ is thus a composite value.

The dependence of magnitude *and* sign of $[\alpha]_\lambda^T$ on solvent is understandable when we consider that molecules in solution are solvated to a greater or lesser extent and that the light interacts with the whole molecular assembly, i.e., with the solute *and* its solvent shell. In this sense, solutions of one and the same substance in two different solvents may be thought of as containing different solute molecules. The dependence of $[\alpha]_\lambda^T$ on temperature has its origin in three factors: the change of density or concentration with temperature, the change in association equilibrium constants (see above) with temperature, and the change in population of the various dissymmetric conformations with temperature.

The dependence of $[\alpha]_\lambda^T$ or $[\phi]_\lambda^T$ on the wave length of light may be understood in terms of the dependence of refractive index on wave length (dispersion) which, in a dissymmetric medium, follows a different course for n_R and n_L, as indicated in Figure 2–6. Since at any given wave length the rotation is proportional to the difference between n_R and n_L, the dependence of specific (or molecular) rotation on wave length (*optical rotatory dispersion* or ORD)

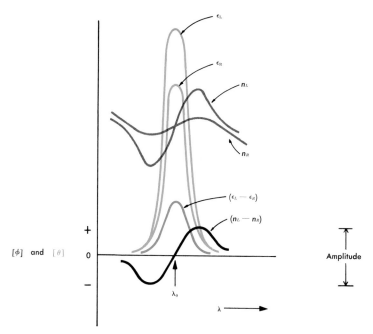

FIGURE 2–6

A positive Cotton effect. The ORD curve ($n_L - n_R$) *reflects the difference of the dispersion curves of left- and right-circularly polarized light; and the circular dichroism curve, the difference* ($\epsilon_L - \epsilon_R$) *of the absorption curves of left and right circularly polarized light. The ordinate represents the magnitude of the various effects. The positive extremum at longer wave lengths is the peak and the negative extremum at shorter wave lengths the trough. The center of the optically active transition is at* λ_o. *For detailed relationship see the text.*

follows a course which is dictated by that difference (Figure 2–6), inclusive of sign. This phenomenon, together with the wave length dependence of circular dichroism (see below), constitutes the *Cotton effect.*

In regions where $n_L > n_R$, $[\alpha]_\lambda^T$ is positive, whereas in regions where $n_L < n_R$, $[\alpha]_\lambda^T$ is negative. When $n_L = n_R$, i.e., at the inflection point of the ORD curve, the optical rotation is zero; this occurs at a wave length which ideally corresponds to the maximum of the relevant absorption band, i.e., to the center of the electronic transition which is responsible for the absorption and optical activity (λ_o). At wave lengths far removed from λ_o the dependence of optical rotation on wave length is often given by a *Drude equa-*

tion, such as $[\alpha]_\lambda^T = A/(\lambda^2 - \lambda_o^2)$, where A is a constant which is characteristic of the solute-solvent system.

The slope of a single ORD curve changes sign at two wave lengths, and these positions are called the *extrema*. If the rotation at the extremum on the longer wave length side (*first extremum*) is more positive than the rotation at the extremum on the shorter wave length side (*second extremum*), the ORD curve is termed positive, the first extremum is called a *peak,* and the second a *trough*. Conversely, in a negative ORD curve the first extremum is a trough and the second a peak. The algebraic difference between peak and trough is the *amplitude*. By this definition the ORD curve in Figure 2–6 is positive. If λ_o occurs at very short wave lengths which are at present instrumentally inaccessible, as in the case of simple hydrocarbons, olefins, ethers, alcohols, etc., the first extremum is not observed and the resulting tail end of the curve is called a *plain curve*. Obviously enantiomers have oppositely signed mirror-image ORD curves. The amplitude of the ORD curve is a measure of the magnitude of the optical rotatory power.

Both magnitude and sign of $[\alpha]_\lambda^T$ are thus dependent on wave length. In order to characterize and identify one of a pair of enantiomers, it is therefore necessary to specify a fixed wave length, and by convention this is 589 mμ, the sodium D-line. Thus, when reference is made to a $(+)-$, $d-$ or (*dextro*)$-$ isomer, or a $(-)-$, $l-$ or (*levo*)$-$ isomer, the sign refers to 589 mμ. This identification must be supplemented by a specification of solvent if the sign is strongly solvent dependent, but this is a relatively rare occurrence. Occasionally, when no rotation is observed at 589 mμ, the enhancement of rotatory power at shorter wave lengths may be used to find the long wave length sign.

We are now prepared to state the conditions for the observation of optical activity. The actual measurement of the optical rotation, *polarimetry* or *spectropolarimetry,* involves large aggregates of molecules and requires a period of time usually of the order of minutes. A necessary condition for the observation of optical activity is therefore not only that the molecules be dissymmetric but that the predominance of one enantiomer over the other be maintained during the period of measurement, i.e., the medium must maintain its dissymmetry during the period of measurement. Optical activity is not observed if the aggregate consists of a statistically equal number of enantiomeric molecules, for the effect of one half of the molecules on the plane of polarized light will be exactly cancelled by the equal and opposite effect of the other half. It is immaterial to our argument whether the enantiomeric molecules suffer rapid interconversion or retain their isomeric integrity: The effect on the optical rotation is the same. However, even assuming a constant predominance of one enantiomer over the other, i.e., *optical stability,* the observation of optical activity depends, operationally, on the magnitude of the specific rotation. This, as we have seen, in turn depends to an important degree on the wave length. It also depends on the extent to which one enantiomer predominates over the other, that is on the *enantiomeric purity.* If the *l*-enantiomer predominates, then (Eq. 2–3):

per cent enantiomeric purity
$$= \frac{\text{moles of } l\text{--form} - \text{moles of } d\text{--form}}{\text{moles of } l\text{--form} + \text{moles of } d\text{--form}} \times 100 \quad (2\text{--}3)$$

It is easily shown that the enantiomeric purity is precisely equal to the *optical purity* (Eq. 2–4):

per cent optical purity
$$= \frac{\text{specific rotation of the enantiomeric mixture}}{\text{specific rotation of one pure enantiomer}} \times 100 \quad (2\text{--}4)$$

Therefore, the smaller the enantiomeric purity (*ergo* optical purity), the smaller is the specific rotation and the less easily is the optical activity detected.

Finally, even if the substance is enantiomerically homogeneous (optical purity = 100%), it may happen for certain structural reasons that the optical activity is immeasurably small at all accessible wave lengths. The substance is then *de facto* optically inactive; such is the case with ethyl-*n*-propyl-*n*-butyl-*n*-hexylmethane.

The observation of optical activity under normal conditions (i.e., in the absence of a strong external magnetic field) *unequivocally signalizes molecular dissymmetry.* This principle, which is one of the cornerstones of stereochemistry, had its origin in the same experiment which was discussed in the preceding section. When Pasteur separately dissolved the enantiomorphous crystals of sodium ammonium tartrate in water, he found that the two solutions were optically active and that the specific rotations were equal in magnitude and opposite in sign. As the result of this and similar observations he arrived at the conclusion, in 1860, that the atoms constituting the molecule tartaric acid, whether arranged in a helical array or at the apices of an irregular tetrahedron, *had* to form a dissymmetric assembly: There was no other way to account for the observed optical activity.

CIRCULAR DICHROISM　　Optical activity also manifests itself in small differences in the molar extinction coefficients ϵ_L and ϵ_R of the circularly polarized components of plane-polarized light. These small differences in ϵ are expressed by the *molecular ellipticity* $[\theta]\lambda^T = 3300(\epsilon_L - \epsilon_R)$. The ellipticity arises from the fact that as one of the circularly polarized beams (corresponding, say, to $\mathbf{E}_R$) is absorbed more than the other, the resultant vector $\mathbf{E}$ no longer oscillates in a plane (whose projection is a line) but instead traces out a flattened helix (whose projection is an ellipse). This is illustrated in Figure 2–7. The ellipticity ψ equals arc tan minor axis/major axis. Since circular birefringence and circular dichroism occur together, it is not strictly the plane of polarization which

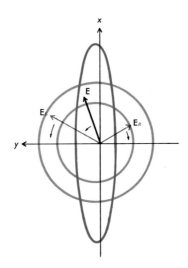

FIGURE 2–7

The outer circle is a projection of the left-handed helix traced out by $\mathbf{E}_L$ *(counterclockwise, away from the observer) and the inner circle a projection of the right-handed helix traced out by* $\mathbf{E}_R$ *(clockwise, away from the observer).* $\mathbf{E}_L$ *and* $\mathbf{E}_R$ *are in phase, but the amplitude of* $\mathbf{E}_R$ *(absorbed to a greater extent) is less than that of* $\mathbf{E}_L$ *(absorbed to a lesser extent). The ellipse is a projection of a flattened left-handed helix (major plane* xz*) traced out by resultant vector* $\mathbf{E}$ *along the z-axis.*

is rotated but the "major plane" of the flattened helix (whose projection is the major axis of the ellipse). However, ψ is usually extremely small, and it is not generally necessary to make this distinction.

The dependence of $[\theta]$ on temperature, solvent, solute, and wave length resembles that of $[\phi]$. The wave length dependence is given by the circular dichroism (CD) curve (Figure 2–6) which has the same sign, positive *or* negative, over the whole wave length range. By convention, when $\epsilon_L > \epsilon_R$, $[\theta]$ is positive. The CD curve is another manifestation of the Cotton effect.

The shape and appearance the circular dichroism curve is closely similar to the absorption curve of the relevant electronic transition; the positions of the wave length maxima of the "reduced" or isolated curves (i.e., curves which are free from overlapping neighboring bands) correspond exactly. The integrated area under the circular dichroism curve is proportional to the *rotational strength* which is a direct measure of the intensity of the dichroism (i.e., of the magnitude of the optical rotatory power) in much the same way as the integrated area under an absorption curve yields a measure of the intensity of absorption (dipole strength).

In contrast to an absorption band, a circular dichroism band is signed, i.e., it can have a positive or a negative maximum. The sign is that of the Cotton effect. The magnitude of the rotational strength is generally reflected in the amplitude of the ORD curve corresponding to the same Cotton effect.

STRUCTURE AND OPTICAL ROTATORY POWER The student may wonder what structural features in a molecule are responsible for the sign of the Cotton effect and the magnitude of its rotational strength. The answer to this question is not uncomplicated, since a given molecule may have several chromophores and one or more electronic transitions which correspond to each of these. For example, a molecule may possess a nitrobenzene ring system and a carbonyl group separated by methylene groups. These chromophores and their various transitions will give rise to several Cotton effects, some of which are positive and some negative. In general, a complex molecule may have numerous *optically active transitions* (i.e., transitions which have Cotton effects), and all the various Cotton effects *cannot* all be of the same sign; this follows because the sum of the rotational strengths of all the absorption bands in a molecule equals zero. The actual ORD or CD curves are thus

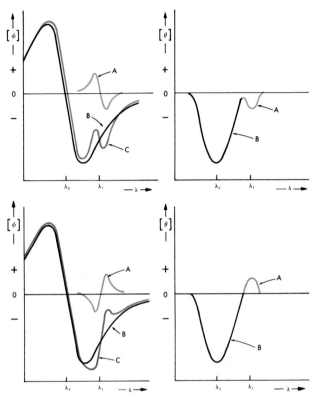

FIGURE 2–8

Schematic drawing of an algebraic summation of two ORD curves. Top left, a low-amplitude negative Cotton effect A *is centered at* λ_1, *and a high-amplitude negative Cotton effect* B *at* λ_2. *Top right, the corresponding CD curves, showing two negative maxima. Bottom left and right, same as at the top, except that the sign of the long wave length Cotton effect is now positive. The summation curve* C *shows that a negative rotation is observed in the long wave length region in either case.*

summation curves of all the Cotton effects, and considerable over-lapping of bands, especially in ORD, is therefore a common occurrence. Indeed, it often happens that the sign of rotation at *D* is determined not by the nearest Cotton effect but by one of opposite sign at shorter wave length (Figure 2–8).

It is convenient in the present context to divide chromophores into two broad divisions. On the one hand, there are chromophores which on grounds of local symmetry are symmetric (i.e., in present context, nondissymmetric) and optically inactive, such as the carbonyl, nitro, and olefin chromophores; these groups may be attached to other groupings, such as alkyl groups, whose electronic transitions are far removed in energy and therefore mix only slightly with those of the chromophores themselves. Such symmetric chromophores may be symmetrically or dissymmetrically perturbed by the extrachromophoric environment, as illustrated in Figure 2–9. *Asymmetrically* or *dissymmetrically perturbed symmetric chromophores* have low rotational strengths. On the other hand, some chromophores are in themselves dissymmetric, and such *inherently dissymmetric chromophores* have high rotational strengths which correspond to allowed electronic transitions; examples are the twisted biphenyls, 1,3-dienes, α,β-unsaturated ketones, nitrobenzenes, aryl sulfoxides, and others (Figure 2–10). These compounds have in common a dissymmetrically twisted π-system which essentially constitutes the entire chromophore. Indeed, high optical activity, e.g., a molecular amplitude of about 100,000° in the near-ultraviolet region of the spectrum, may be taken as *prima facie* evidence for the presence of an inherently dissymmetric chromo-

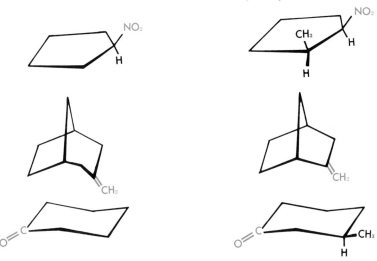

FIGURE 2–9

Some examples of symmetric chromophores (marked in color). The perturbing environment is nondissymmetric (left) and dissymmetric (right).

phore, i.e., for a twisted π-system. It should be noted that formal conjugation is not essential, since homoconjugated systems (e.g., dissymmetric 1,4-dienes and β,γ-unsaturated ketones) have also been known to give rise to the high optical rotatory power which is characteristic of inherently dissymmetric chromophores (Figure 2–10).

The sign of the Cotton effect of an inherently dissymmetric chromophore directly depends on the chirality of the chromophore. The sign of the Cotton effect of a dissymmetrically perturbed symmetric chromophore depends on the chirality of the perturbing environment.

It must be stressed that this classification of optically active chromophores is purely a matter of convenience since, from the theoretical point of view, either outlook must ultimately lead to the

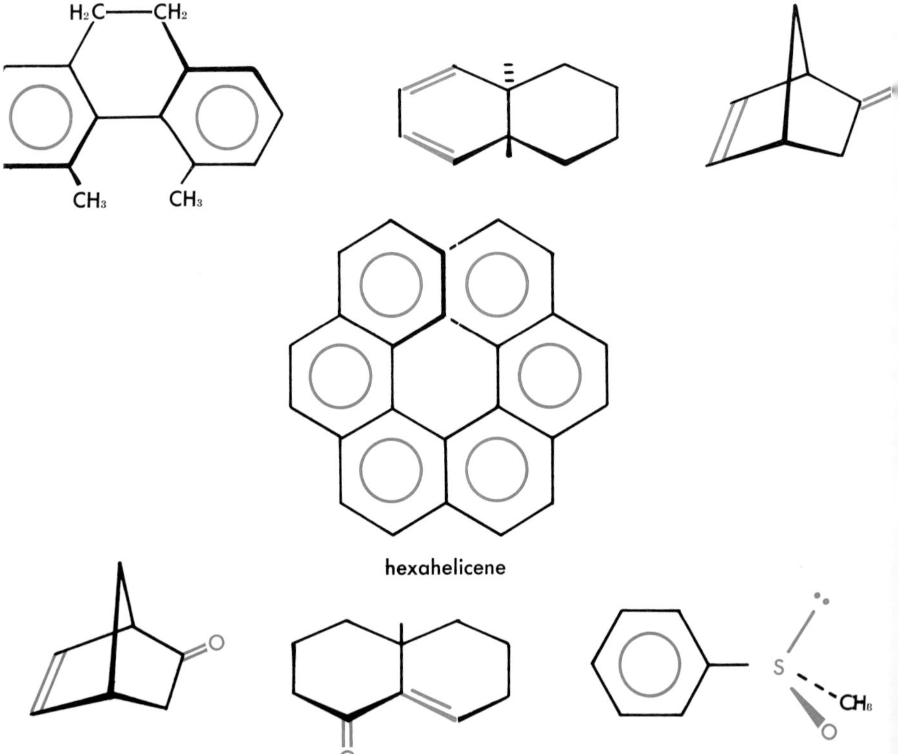

hexahelicene

FIGURE 2–10

Some examples of inherently dissymmetric chromophores (marked in color).

same result. These viewpoints are thus not mutually exclusive but refer to limiting situations which are separated by a continuum of possibilities.

2–3   Diastereomers and Racemic Forms

We noted in Section 2–1 that diastereomers may be distinguished without recourse to a dissymmetric handle. The intramolecular interactions in diastereomers are different in all of the possible conformations, and the geometry (e.g., bond lengths, bond angles, angles of torsion) of the equilibrium conformations of diastereomers must therefore also be different. Diastereomers have different energy contents: they differ in their heats of formation, combustion, and (where applicable) hydrogenation (cf. Figure 2–11). They differ in all of their spectral properties (UV, IR, NMR, mass spectra). Their crystal structures (i.e., packing arrangements) differ, *ergo* their melting points, densities, and solu-

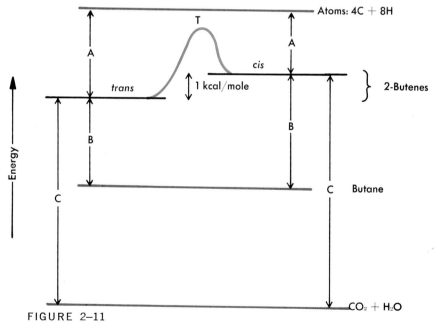

FIGURE 2–11

Some energy relationships in isomeric 2-butenes: A, heat of formation; B, heat of hydrogenation; C, heat of combustion; T, transition state for interconversion (hypothetical).

bilities differ. The liquids have different boiling points, refractive indices, densities, viscosities. Diastereomers differ in dipole moments, dielectric constants, adsorptivities on alumina, acid or base strengths: In short, diastereomers, like constitutional isomers, differ in every single physical property and are conspicuously different chemical entities.

Although the descriptive chemistry of functional groups of diastereomers is the same, rates of reaction and hence ratio of products in competing reactions must be different, for reasons which may be most simply illustrated by the example of the interconversion of two diastereomers (Figure 2–11). If the interconversion is for the sake of simplicity pictured as a one-step process, i.e., if the rate-determining step is also the product-determining step, the transition state will then be the same for the forward and for the backward reaction. Since the energy of activation is the difference between the energies of the ground state and the transition state, and since the ground state energies of the two diastereomers are different, it follows that the activation energies and hence the rates of reaction are different for the forward and the backward steps. It might be noted that in the similar interconversion of two enantiomers, the energies of activation and hence the rates of reaction of the forward and backward steps are the same.

Diastereomers may be (but need not be) dissymmetric. If dissymmetric, each diastereomer in turn exists in two enantiomeric forms. The optical rotations of two optically stable and optically pure diastereomers (nonenantiomeric isomers) of the same substance must differ in magnitude and may (but need not) differ in sign of rotation and associated Cotton effect. Enantiomers of the same substance must have rotations and Cotton effects which are identical in magnitude but opposite in sign.

Intramolecular interactions differ in individual diastereomers or diastereomeric conformations. Similarly, intermolecular interactions differ in diastereomeric mixtures, i.e., in any two mixtures which are composed of the same two enantiomers but which differ in optical purity. Such mixtures must therefore also differ to a greater or lesser extent in the physical properties listed above. The particular mixture which is composed of equimolar parts of two enantiomeric forms is called the *racemic (rac.) form,* or the *dl-* or *(±)-pair.* The difference between racemic forms and the enantiomerically pure components may be likened to the difference between a box filled with pairs of gloves and one filled with right-handed gloves only. The packing (density) will be different. The energies of interaction will be different because the topology of interactions between (*a*) two right hands and (*b*) a right and a left hand is very different (compare shaking a right hand and a left hand, using the same hand [i.e., handle] each time). Therefore, the properties of the two assemblages will be different. Seen in this light one would expect to observe differences in physical properties between racemic forms and the corresponding enantiomers, and in fact this is particularly noticeable in the melting point and solubility behavior, properties which are related to the packing in the crystal lattice, i.e., to the molecular analog of our box of gloves.

Generally, racemic forms are either simple mixtures (*conglomerates*) or distinct compounds (*racemates*) of the component enantiomers. The mixtures are eutectic mixtures, and the melting points of conglomerates are therefore always below those of the component enantiomers (whose melting points are of course identical). Racemates may melt above, below, or at the same temperature as the enantiomers. The melting point of a racemate is depressed by admixture with one of the enantiomers, and in this manner may be distinguished from a conglomerate. Racemates, unlike conglomerates, often have infrared spectra (in the solid state) and crystal structures which differ markedly from those of the enantiomers.

In the preceding paragraph the contrast between racemic forms and enantiomeric components has been made with reference to the crystalline state. In dilute solution, the distinction between racemic and enantiomeric forms disappears because the diastereomeric interactions are minimized and so are the consequences of such interactions. As a result, the spectra and other physical properties (except for optical activity) of solutions of racemic and enantiomeric forms are indistinguishable, even though in principle they cannot be identical except at infinite dilution. Similarly, solutions of enantiomeric mixtures of varying optical purities have indistinguishable spectra and other physical properties (except for optical activity).

A last point concerns the formation of *dl*-pairs. Racemic forms result from (*a*) direct synthesis in the absence of dissymmetric influences, (*b*) mixing of equimolar quantities of the enantiomers, (*c*) racemization. *Racemization* is the irreversible formation of *dl*-pairs by the reversible interconversion of enantiomers, regardless of mechanism. The driving force for the spontaneous process is the entropy of mixing ($R \ln 2$), which lowers the free energy of the *dl*-pair (by about 0.4 kcal/mole at room temperature) relative to that of the components. Operationally, racemization is the complete loss of optical activity with time. It is instructive to compare this process with the reversible interconversion of diastereomers (*epimerization*). Since the equilibrium mixture in this case is not necessarily optically inactive, this process may involve, operationally, a *change* of optical rotation with time (*mutarotation*), including, possibly, a change in sign.

2–4 Torsional Stereoisomerism

It will be recalled (Section 2–1) that stereoisomers may also be classified according to the nature and magnitude of the energy barrier which separates them. There exists a class of stereoisomers whose relationship is such that they may be interconverted—at least conceptually if not always in practice—by the simple operation of torsion about a bond axis. This torsion may take place about a formal single bond or about a formal double bond, as illustrated in Figures 1–21 and 1–22, respectively.

A given isomer may, by our definition, have innumerable conformations. For example, one equilibrium conformation exists for each of the three isomers of *n*-butane (as in Figure 1–21), but in addition there exists a number, in principle infinite, of other conformations which corresponds to the number of positions (defined by the value of the dihedral angle of torsion) between adjacent maxima in the potential energy curve. At room temperature the collection of conformations between adjacent maxima is most heavily populated by the equilibrium conformation corresponding to V_{min}, and this conformation lends its name to the entire collection.

In *n*-butane the two dissymmetric *gauche* isomers are enantiomers; together these constitute a rapidly interconverting *dl*-pair. Even at very low temperatures the interconversion is too fast to permit the isolation of the separate mirror-image forms. From Figure 1–21 it may be noted that two paths are possible for this interconversion. The *anti*-isomer is a nondissymmetric diastereomer of the two *gauche* forms.

Isomers which may be interconverted by torsion around a single bond are variously referred to as *rotomers* (or *rotamers*), *conformers,* and *conformational isomers*. A more descriptive if more unwieldy term might be *torsional single bond isomers*.

The discussion just presented for butane applies with equal force to torsion around double bonds. In 2-butene (Figure 1–22) the *cis*- and *trans*-forms are nondissymmetric diastereomers. At room temperature most of the molecules have the planar or near-planar conformations corresponding to the two values of V_{min}. Isomers which may be interconverted by torsion around double bonds are classically termed *geometric isomers* or *cis-trans-isomers*. The term *torsional double bond isomers* is more descriptive but too cumbersome. We shall mainly use the term "geometric" in the foregoing sense, implying hindered rotation around a double bond, though it may be extended to cases of ring *cis-trans*-isomerism such as in the *cis*- and *trans*-1,4-dimethylcyclohexanes.

Torsional isomerism need not be restricted to single-bond and double-bond isomers. For example, torsional isomerism is conceivable for ferrocene (exercise 1–4), yet the nature of the bond or bonds associated with the torsional C_5 axis is assuredly neither "single" nor "double." Nevertheless, the two major categories account for the vast majority of torsional stereoisomers encountered in organic chemistry.

TORSIONAL SINGLE BOND (CONFORMATIONAL) ISOMERISM
Isomerism of this type has been discussed in section 1–5 and in the preceding paragraphs. The barrier height, which determines whether the isomers are separable under ordinary conditions, is intimately related to the molecular constitution, and few generalizations are possible, except the following: To date no conformational isomers have been separated in which the molecule does not also contain double bonds, bicyclic ring systems, or benzene rings. It would appear that double bonds and the above rings systems introduce an element of rigidity into the molecular framework which effectively increases the potential barrier to conformational interconversion; in the absence of these or equivalent structural features the great flexibility of the molecule permits facile passage over the energy barrier. However, even when conformational isomers cannot be separated, their presence can sometimes be detected and their rate of interconversion be gauged by the technique of nuclear magnetic resonance (NMR) spectroscopy.

When a sample of an organic substance is placed into a strong magnetic field, the field which is experienced by certain nuclei (notably ^1H and ^{19}F) depends on the diamagnetic shielding of the surrounding "screening" electrons. The difference between the experienced and the applied fields is expressed by the "chemical shift" of the nucleus. The chemical shift is therefore a measure of the effectiveness of shielding by a particular chemical environment and thus depends on the stereochemistry of the nucleus. This may be illustrated by the example of propene, which has four kinds of protons, as shown (Formula I):

The environment of this proton →(1) H   H   (3)
is diastereomeric with the

environment of this proton →(2) H   CH₃   (4)

$$\begin{array}{ccc} H & & H \quad (3) \\ \diagdown & & \diagup \\ & C{=}C & \qquad \mathrm{I}\\ \diagup & & \diagdown \\ H & & CH_3 \quad (4) \end{array}$$

Each proton "sees" (i.e., experiences) a different chemical environment, and analysis of the spectrum would reveal four different chemical shifts. Of particular interest is the relationship between the similar protons 1, 2, and 3. The relationship between 1 and 3, and between 2 and 3, is constitutional; the relationship between 1 and 2, however, is purely spatial. Protons such as 1 and 2 are therefore conveniently dubbed *diastereomeric protons.*

The concept of diastereomeric protons may be understood in another way. If the two diastereomeric protons were exactly equivalent, replacement of either one by a deuterium nucleus should give the identical compound. In fact, replacement of one or the other of the two diastereomeric protons by a deuterium nucleus results in the formation of conventional diastereomers (Formula II).

$$\begin{array}{cccccc} H & & H & D & & H \\ \diagdown & & \diagup & \diagdown & & \diagup \\ & C{=}C & & & C{=}C & \qquad \mathrm{II} \\ \diagup & & \diagdown & \diagup & & \diagdown \\ D & & CH_3 & H & & CH_3 \end{array}$$

In the case of rapidly interconverting isomers, the NMR spectrum at room temperature may show an average proton or fluorine resonance signal. However, as the temperature is lowered and the rate of passage over the energy barrier is slowed, the environments of the individual protons or fluorine nuclei are frozen out; the signal broadens and finally separates into the signals of the individual protons or fluorine nuclei.

To illustrate these and related points, let us first consider the case of 1,1-difluoro-1,2-dibromo-2,2-dichloroethane, for which three conformational isomers may be written (Formula III):

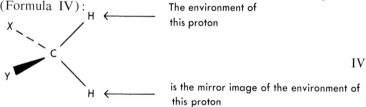

Anti   Gauche

In each of the *gauche* enantiomers, the fluorine nuclei are diastereomeric in the sense explained above. However, in the *anti*-isomer the relationship of the two fluorine nuclei is no longer diastereomeric. Although the two fluorine nuclei have not become equivalent, they now experience mirror-image environments. This means that they can be only distinguished under dissymmetric conditions (section 2–1), and NMR is therefore incapable of differentiating between such nuclei. This case of enantiomerically related nuclei may be generalized to that of any molecule of type $Cxyz_2$, where x and y are different nondissymmetric groupings and z_2 are the *enantiomeric nuclei*. In cases where the enantiomeric nuclei are protons, we may speak of *enantiomeric protons* (Formula IV):

H ⟵ The environment of this proton

$$X_{\diagdown} \quad \diagup$$
$$C$$
$$Y\blacktriangleleft \quad \diagdown$$

IV

H ⟵ is the mirror image of the environment of this proton

The concept of enantiomeric protons may also be explained in another way. If the two enantiomeric protons were exactly equivalent, replacement of either one by a deuterium nucleus should give the identical compound. In fact, replacement of the enantiomeric protons by deuterium nuclei results in the formation of conventional enantiomers (Formula V). In contrast to diastereomeric protons, a σ plane bisects the H—C—H angle between enantiomeric protons.

Let us now return to the case of 1,1-difluoro-1,2-dibromo-2,2-dichloroethane. At room temperature there is a single sharp fluorine signal, but at $-80°$ there are several lines. This means that at lower temperatures the rate of torsional oscillation has been slowed to the point where the NMR resonances of the diastereomeric fluorine nuclei in the *gauche* forms become discernible, whereas at room temperature the rotation is so rapid that the two fluorine nuclei give the appearance of one "average" atom.

A related example is the conversion of 3,4-homotropylidene into itself by a Cope rearrangement (Formula VI):

Since the product is indistinguishable from the starting material, this process may be called a *degenerate interconversion* (or *identity-reaction*). The vibrations of ethane (torsion) and ammonia (inversion) further illustrate this term.

In 3,4-homotropylidene, the ten hydrogen nuclei differ constitutionally, diastereomerically (1/2, 6/7), or enantiomerically (3/3, 4/4, 5/5). At $-50°$, when the interconversion is very slow (1 sec^{-1}), seven signals are discerned as might have been expected (1,2,3,4,5,6,7). At elevated temperatures, however, when the interconversion is rapid (e.g., 1000 sec^{-1} at 180°), protons 3 and 5, 1 and 6, and 2 and 7 become equivalent on the average, so that only four signals remain (1/6, 2/7, 3/5, and 4). Such compounds are said to have *fluxional structures*.

The principal *conceptual* (as opposed to practical) difference between these fluxional structures and the rapidly interconverting torsional conformational isomers is that in the former, the interconversions require that covalent bonds be made and broken.

In other studies, it has been found that rotation is slowed around the central C—N bond in N,N-dimethylacetamide when the temperature is lowered (Formula VII).

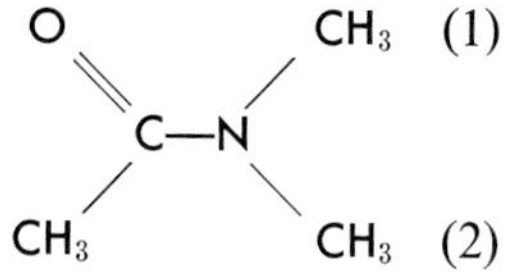

VII

The diastereomeric methyl protons 1 and 2 are averaged out at room temperature. However, at lower temperatures the residence time of each of the two kinds of protons is sufficiently extended so that the difference in the chemical shifts becomes apparent. The nature of the torsional barrier in amides is believed to be related to the bonding interaction of neighboring $2p$-orbitals on carbon and nitrogen. Such interaction, which is directional, would tend to keep the molecule in a planar conformation and would give rise to conformational isomerism in molecules such as 1,3-dienes, esters, nitrites, and amides. The terminology s-*cis* and s-*trans* (s = single bond) is reserved for such cases (Formula VIII):

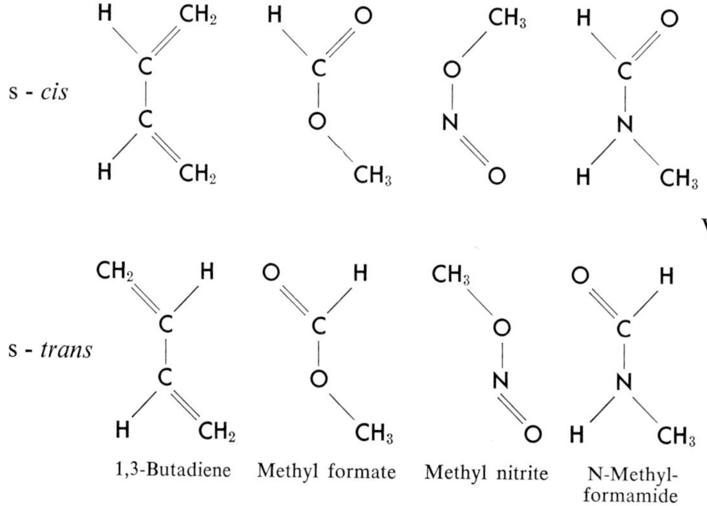

VIII

1,3-Butadiene   Methyl formate   Methyl nitrite   N-Methyl-formamide

Conformational isomerism is an important feature in the stereochemistry of cyclohexanes. Cyclohexane is the alicyclic structure most frequently encountered in natural products, and it has for this reason been studied more extensively than any other ring system.

Two principal conformational isomers of cyclohexane can be distinguished in which the angle strain is at a minimum: the *rigid form* and the *flexible form*. The rigid form, also called the *chair form*, has D_{3d} symmetry (Figure 1–19). Torsional strain is at a minimum in this isomer: The bonds are almost perfectly staggered (the C—C—C angles are about 111° and the molecule is therefore somewhat flattened). The twelve bonds to hydrogen are divided into two sets: Six are essentially parallel to the C_3 axis (the *axial* bonds, *a*), and six are more nearly perpendicular to the C_3 axis (the *equatorial* bonds, *e*). These bonding arrangements are interchangeable (Figure 2–12). In order to effect the inter-conversion it is necessary to deform the chair conformation. This deformation, which introduces angle, torsional, and nonbonded strain, brings the molecule into a transition state conformation which has an energy content 11 kcal/mole above that of V_{min} for the rigid isomer (Figure 2–13). Past this barrier lies the flexible isomer in which axial and equatorial bonds rapidly interchange relative positions in space. The flexible isomer exists preferentially in the D_2 *twist form* (Figure 2–13), which interconverts into itself or into its enantiomer *via* the C_{2v} *boat* transition state (Figure 2–13). The twist form is less stable than the chair form by 5.5 kcal/mole; this means that at 25° there are 10,000 chair conformations for each twist conformation.

The flexible isomer may convert back into chair form, with *a*- and *e*-bonds interchanged. Since the product (chair) is indistinguishable from the starting (chair) material, this is clearly a degenerate interconversion.

Although the interconversion of *a*- and *e*-bonds is extremely rapid at room temperature, the process is noticeably slowed at

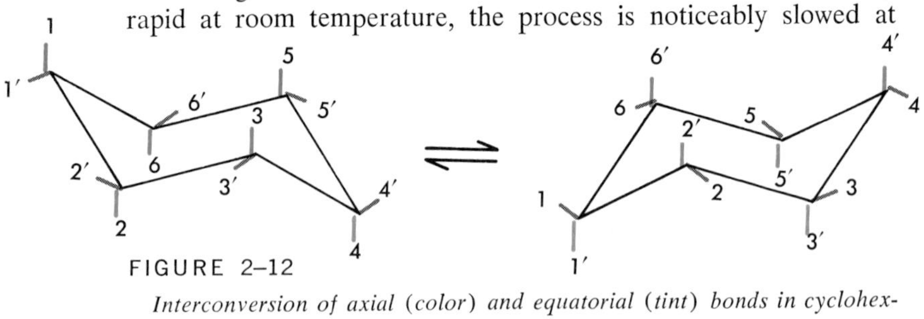

FIGURE 2–12

Interconversion of axial (color) and equatorial (tint) bonds in cyclohexane.

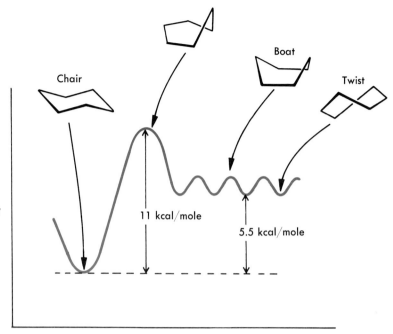

FIGURE 2–13

Torsional isomerism in cyclohexane.

lower temperatures. Thus at $+35°$ the NMR spectrum 1,1-difluorocyclohexane shows the presence of only one "average" fluorine atom; however, at $-110°$ the NMR spectrum has changed completely, since at that temperature the residence time of the diastereomeric fluorine nuclei is sufficiently long to permit the recording of a different signal from each.

In monosubstituted cyclohexanes *two* diastereomeric chair forms are possible, depending on whether the substituent is in the axial or equatorial position; the isomers are interconvertible *via* the common flexible form. The relative stability of the *a*- and *e*-isomers depends on the nature of the substituent. If the substituent is an alkyl group, the *e*-isomer is the more stable form by an amount which increases with the size of the alkyl group: 1.7, 1.8, 2.1 and greater than 4.4 kcal/mole for methyl, ethyl, isopropyl, and *t*-butyl groups, respectively. Inspection of models reveals that the difference in energy originates in nonbonded interactions of the axial alkyl group on C-1 with the axial hydrogen atoms on C-3 and C-5. The quantitative information cited above can be expressed in the following equivalent terms: At 25°, there are 18, 21, 35, and more than 1600 *e*-forms for each *a*-form, respectively.

In cases where the substituent is not an alkyl group, the *e*-isomer is still the more stable form, but the preference may in some cases be very slight: Thus the *e*- and *a*-forms of bromocyclohexane exist in roughly equal amounts at equilibrium.

We remarked earlier that conformational isomers have been separated only in those cases in which the molecule also contains structural elements which impart rigidity to the molecule, in particular double bonds and benzene rings. Such separable torsional single bond isomers are referred to as *atropisomers*.

Atropisomerism is most commonly encountered among the biphenyls. We saw in Figures 1–11 and 1–12 how enantiomerism is possible for such compounds, and we now add the information that interconversion of the enantiomers is rendered difficult by the necessity of forcing bulky *ortho* substituents (in the examples cited, the halogen atoms) past one another in the transition state. Accordingly, a high activation energy barrier separates the enantiomers. Such isomers exhibit restricted or hindered rotation (i.e., torsion) around the pivot bond due to excessive nonbonded interaction (*overcrowding*) in the transition state.

The following two conditions obtain for atropisomerism in biphenyls in which the *ortho*-positions are not bridged: First, neither ring may possess a σ plane perpendicular to the plane of the ring, and second, the blocking groups must be bulky enough so as to prevent facile interconversion. In this connection, it must be remembered that *two* diastereomeric transition state conformations are always available for the interconversion of such enantiomers. For example, 2,2′-dimethylbiphenyl can interconvert into its enantiomer either *via* the cisoid or *via* the transoid transition state conformation (Figure 2–14). In the cisoid conformation overcrowding is severe, but in the transoid conformation the methyl groups easily slip past the hydrogen atoms. Racemization therefore takes place with greater ease by the transoid path. This is not to say that 2,2′-disubstituted (as contrasted with the more common 2,2′,6-trisubstituted or 2,2′,6,6′-tetrasubstituted) biphenyls cannot be separated into enantiomeric forms: optically active 1,1′-binaphthyl is known, and so are optically active derivatives of 2,2′-diiodobiphenyls. These compounds, as expected, are optically unstable.

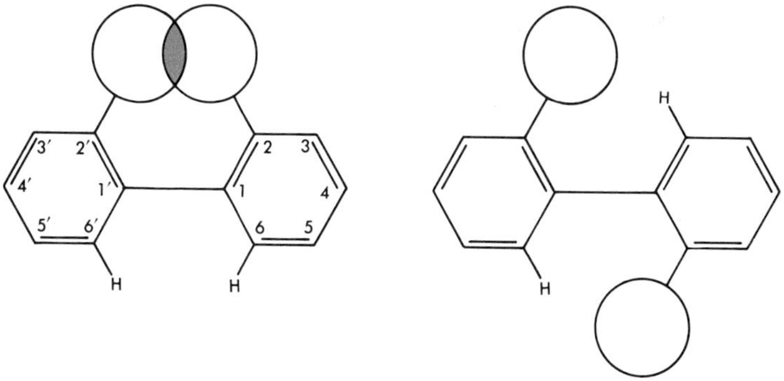

FIGURE 2–14

Two possible transition states for the interconversion of biphenyl enantiomers with 2,2'-substituents. Left, cisoid. Right, transoid. Overcrowding is schematically indicated by the colored area.

Overcrowding need not be the principal cause of restricted rotation, especially in biphenyls in which the *ortho*-positions are bridged: Excessive angle strain in the transition state of racemization may also be responsible for observed enantiomerism. The enantiomeric biphenyls shown in Figure 1–16 have been separated; they are optically active and rapidly interconvert at room temperature. By building suitable models, it is easily seen that the barrier to racemization is largely due to angle strain. The feature of

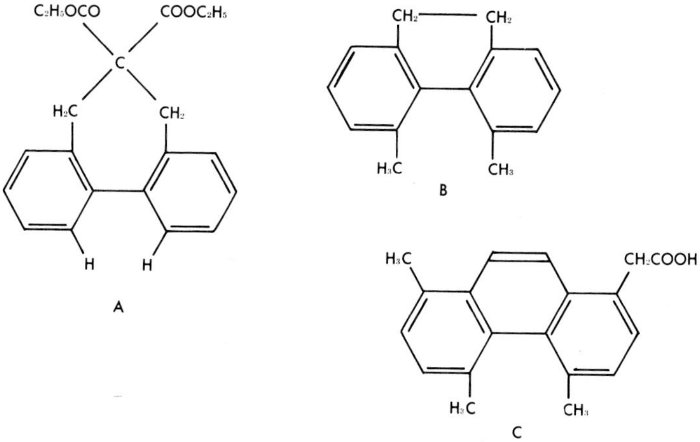

FIGURE 2–15

Some singly bridged optically active biphenyls. A, transition state of racemization destabilized principally by angle strain. B and C, ground and transition states destabilized by overcrowding, but the latter far more than the former.

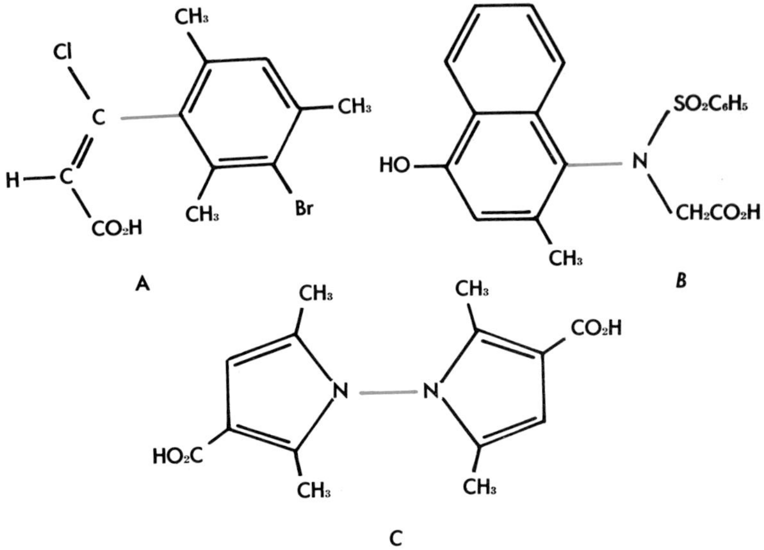

FIGURE 2–16

Some optically active compounds exhibiting biphenyl-like atropisomerism. Pivot bonds are marked in color. The planar conformations are overcrowded.

double bridging shown in Figure 1–16 is not essential; even a single bridge suffices, with or without blocking substituents (Figure 2–15).

The concept of biphenyl atropisomerism is readily extended to systems which differ formally in structure but in which the stereochemical requirements for atropisomerism closely resemble those in optically active biphenyls (Figure 2–16). However, the attribute of being "biphenyl-like" is not a necessary one for the condition of atropisomerism. For example, in tri-*o*-thymotide (Figure 1–15), the propeller-like (C_3) enantiomers rapidly interconvert at room temperature, but not so rapidly as to preclude polarimetric observation of this process. Atropisomerism has been demonstrated in a variety of other structural types (Figure 2–17).

Atropisomerism does not necessarily imply enantiomerism: The separate forms may instead be diastereomers. This is illustrated in Figure 2–18 for the case of variously substituted terphenyls. For each of the substitution patterns shown, the *cis*- and *trans*-forms are diastereomers, and additional isomerism depends on the particular substitution pattern. Thus in *A*, *cis*- and *trans*-forms are both dissymmetric and may therefore each exist in enantiomeric forms. In *B* the *cis*-form is dissymmetric (two enan-

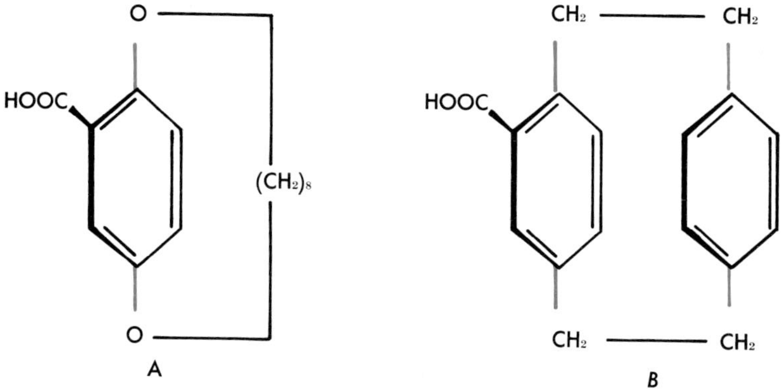

FIGURE 2–17

Examples of optically active atropisomers: A, *an ansa compound;* B, *a paracyclophane. Pivot bonds are marked in color.*

tiomers), but the *trans*-form has S_2 symmetry and is therefore non-dissymmetric and optically inactive (an optically inactive diastereomer is called a *meso*-form). In C it is the *trans* isomer which is dissymmetric whereas the *cis*-form is the *meso*-isomer (C_s), and in D both isomers are *meso* (*cis*-C_{2v} and *trans*-C_{2h}). In short: A has two *dl*-pairs, B and C have one *dl*-pair and one *meso*-form, and D has two *meso*-forms.

A restricted biphenyl has been prepared in enantiomerically homogeneous form in which the 2- and 2′-positions are occupied by —CH_3 groups, and the 6- and 6′-positions by —CD_3 groups. This compound, like ethyl-*n*-propyl-*n*-butyl-*n*-hexylmethane, is dissymmetric but exhibits no optical activity at any wave length, as measured with currently available spectropolarimeters: This illustrates the general principle that dissymmetry and enantiomeric homogeneity are no guarantee of measurable optical activity.

TORSIONAL DOUBLE BOND (GEOMETRIC) ISOMERISM   The pivot bonds of geometric isomers, like those of conformational isomers, may be formed between two like or two unlike atoms (Figure 2–19). Other things being equal, these stereoisomers are separated by much higher energy barriers than single-bond isomers, for reasons discussed above (Sec. 1–5), and they are therefore usually quite stable at room temperature.

In principle, 2^n diastereomers are possible for constitutionally unsymmetrical acyclic olefins with n double bonds, e.g., $CH_3CH =$ CH—CH = CH—COOH ($n = 2$), as illustrated in Table 2–1 for $n = 1$ to 4. This Table also introduces the term "configuration."

INTRODUCTION TO STEREOCHEMISTRY

82

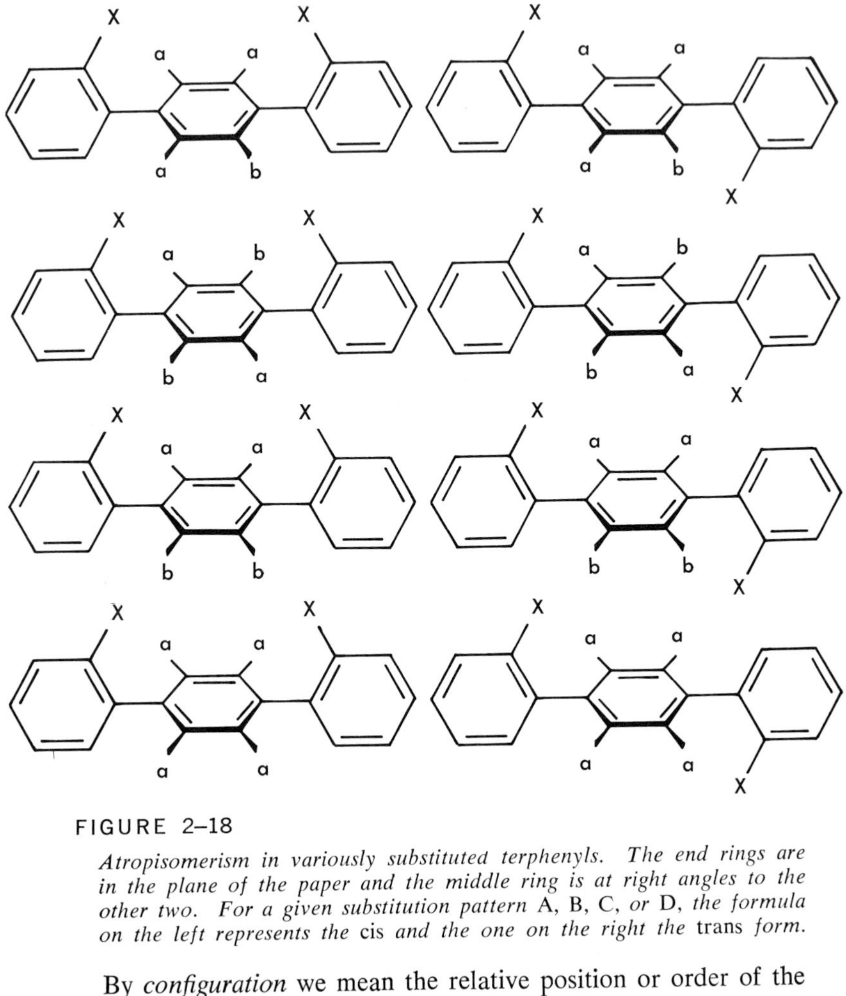

FIGURE 2–18

Atropisomerism in variously substituted terphenyls. The end rings are in the plane of the paper and the middle ring is at right angles to the other two. For a given substitution pattern A, B, C, or D, the formula on the left represents the cis *and the one on the right the* trans *form.*

By *configuration* we mean the relative position or order of the arrangement of atoms in space which characterizes a particular stereoisomer. For example, enantiomers differ characteristically in their configurations because their chiralities are opposite: Enantiomers have "opposite" configurations. Diastereomers have configurations which, though not opposite, are different. The designation of diastereomeric configurations generally presents no problem; in the present case the notations *cis* and *trans* in the Table refer to the configuration of the respective diastereomers.

Although the *trans*-isomer is generally the more stable form, the *cis*-isomer often predominates among naturally occurring nonconjugated fatty acids. For example, oleic, linoleic, linolenic, and

TABLE 2-1 ■

Diastereomers Possible for Constitutionally Unsymmetrical Olefins

Configuration

Number of double bonds (n)	cis (C)				trans (T)			
1	C				T			
2	CC		CT		TC		TT	
3	CCC	CCT	CTC	CTT	TCC	TCT	TTC	TTT
4	CCCC CCCT	CCTC CCTT	CTCC CTCT	CTTC CTTT	TCCC TCCT	TCTC TCTT	TTCC TTCT	TTTC TTTT

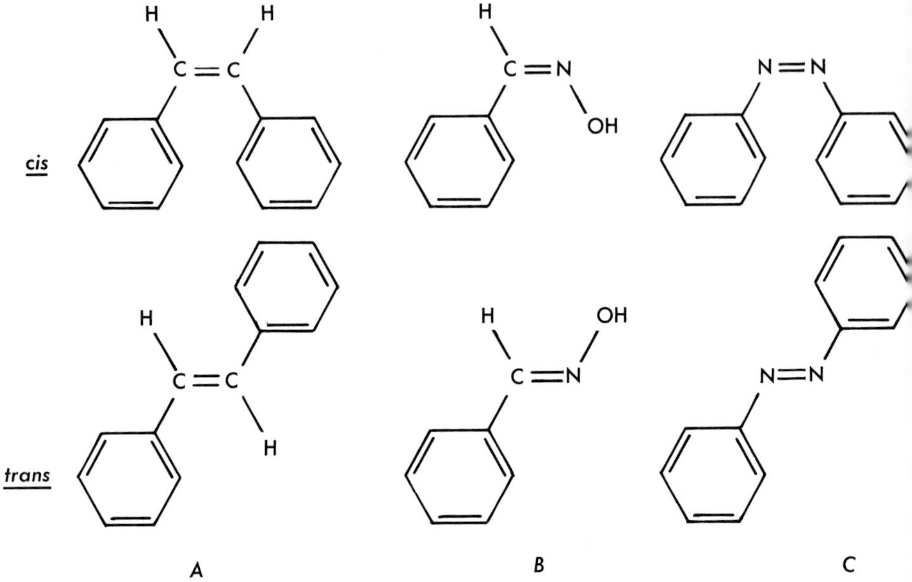

FIGURE 2–19

Geometric isomers. A, stilbene; B, benzaldoxime; C, azobenzene.

arachidonic acids are the all-*cis*-isomers of mono-, di-, tri-, and tetra-olefins, respectively, derived from octadecanoic acid (see also page 38).

The number of diastereomers for constitutionally symmetrical olefins with n double bonds (e.g., $CH_3CH = CH—CH = CH—CH_3$, $n = 2$) is $2^{(n-1)} + 2^{(n-2)/2}$ when n is even, and $2^{(n-1)} + 2^{(n-1)/2}$ when n is odd. The naturally occurring compounds squalene and lycopene, both all-*trans*-isomers, exemplify these two categories (Formula IX).

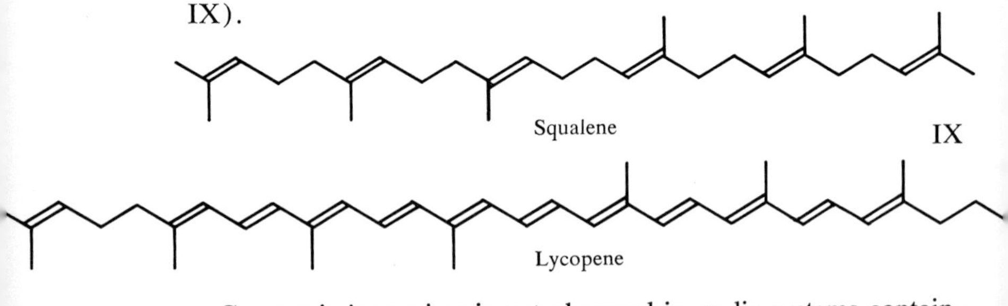

Squalene

IX

Lycopene

Geometric isomerism is not observed in cyclic systems containing fewer than eight carbon atoms, since the presence of a *trans*-double bond in a small ring imposes an intolerable strain on the molecule. The smallest ring thus far known to accommodate a *trans*-double bond is eight-membered. This arrangement is less stable than the *cis*-isomer by 9 kcal/mole (coincidentally the same amount by which, in the acyclic series, *cis*-2,2,5,5-tetramethyl-3-hexene is less stable than the *trans*-isomer [Section 1–5]). As the ring size increases, this difference in stability becomes less extreme, and for cycloundecene and larger ring systems the stability relationship is like that in the acyclic series, i.e., the *trans*-isomer is more stable than the *cis*-isomer.

We had seen earlier that atropisomerism ordinarily gives rise to enantiomers, though the formation of diastereomers was not necessarily excluded. In contrast, geometric isomerism is most often associated with diastereoisomerism, though here again a few examples are known in which restricted rotation around a double bond results in the formation of enantiomers (sometimes referred to as *geometric enantiomers*). For example, the enantiomers shown in Figure 2–20 result from torsion around a double bond in which the component σ-bond is essentially sp^2–sp^2. Similarly, enantiomeric allenes (Figure 1–12) may *in principle* be interconverted through torsion around a double bond in which the component σ-bond is sp–sp^2. The structural condition for enantiomerism in substituted allenes ($>$C$=$C$=$C$<$) is the same as that for *cis-trans*-isomerism in substituted ethylenes ($>$C$=$C$<$) or cumulenes ($>$C$=$C$=$C$=$C$<$), *viz.*, that interchange of substituents on either one of the terminal atoms must not result in the identical stereoisomer. Note that interconversion of diastereoisomeric *cis-trans* cumulenes of type xyC$=$C$=$C$=$Cxy involves torsion around a double bond in which the component σ-bond may be either sp–sp^2 or sp–sp.

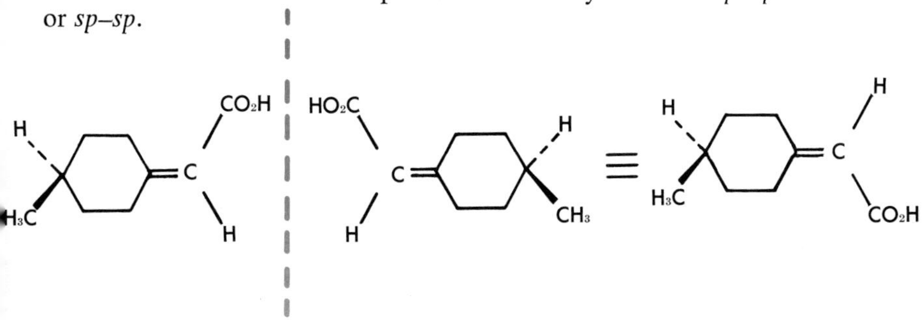

FIGURE 2–20

An example of enantiomerism arising from geometric isomerism. The cyclohexane conformation is not indicated.

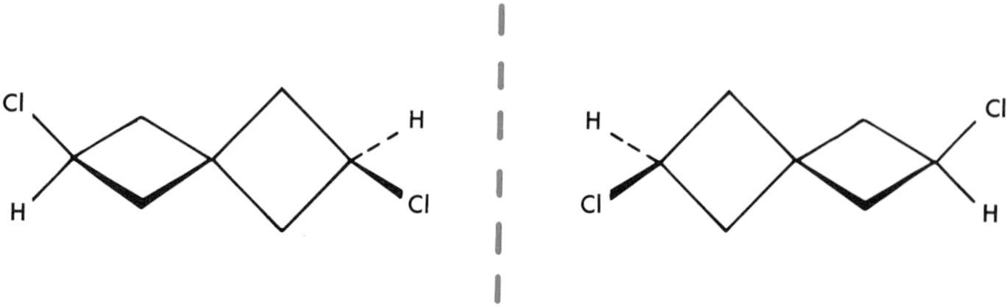

FIGURE 2–21

Enantiomeric spiranes analogous to the allenes in Figure 1–12.

As implied above in the comparison between allenes and the enantiomers shown in Figure 2–20, a double bond is geometrically equivalent to a ring (disregarding conformational isomerism). According to this point of view, the stereochemistry of the allene system is not essentially changed when we go to systems having two rings in place of double bonds; such systems are called *spiranes* (Figure 2–21). The central atom in a spirane may be C, N^+, Si, or any other tetrahedral atom.

The preceding classification of torsional isomers into single-bond and double-bond isomers may be justified on the basis of its general usefulness, but, as in most other classifications, occasional instances of ambiguity cannot be avoided. For example, our classification breaks down in the case of *trans*-cycloöctene. This highly strained molecule (see above) exists in optically stable enantiomeric forms having C_2 symmetry (Figure 2–22) which could *in principle* interconvert by two independent paths: (*a*) torsion around the double bond, *via* the *cis*-isomer; (*b*) torsion around single bonds only, i.e., a looping motion of the hexamethylene chain over a 180° arc, starting on one side of the double bond and ending up on the other. This last alternative becomes most probable when the loop is large enough, a condition which is met by the octamethylene chain in *trans*-cyclodecene. This compound racemizes with extreme ease by the second mechanism, implying conformational stereoisomerism.

2–5 **Stereoisomerism Resulting from Asymmetric Atoms Designation of Configuration at Asymmetric Atoms**

We have seen (Sec. 1–4) that an *asymmetric carbon atom* is one to which four substituents are attached which differ in the sense that exchange of any two gives a new stereoisomer. When the four

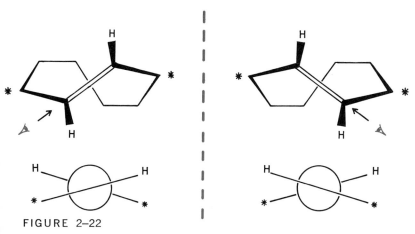

FIGURE 2–22

Enantiomeric trans-*cyclooctenes. *Bottom, Newman projections along the double-bond axis (asterisks identify carbon atoms corresponding to the perspective drawing).*

substituents differ in the number or kind of atoms they contain and there is but one such carbon atom in the molecule, the carbon atom and the molecule are both asymmetric and the substance may exist in enantiomeric forms. Such compounds are optically active within the limitations stated in section 2–2. The difference among the substituents may be merely an isotopic one; thus CH_3CHDOH (ethanol-1-*d*) is optically active. Furthermore, though we are in this text concerned with the stereochemistry of carbon, it may be noted that numerous organic compounds are known which owe their optical activity to other *asymmetric atoms,* such as configurationally stable tetracoordinate silicon, germanium, nitrogen, phosphorus, and arsenic (the 'onium salts in the last three cases) and even configurationally stable tricoordinate arsenic, antimony, sulfur, and phosphorus. If, as in the case of the tricoordinate compounds, an unshared electron pair is formally regarded as the fourth substituent, the generalizations which are made for the asymmetric carbon atom may be extended *in toto* to all of the asymmetric atoms other than carbon, examples of which are shown in Figure 2–23. The simplest asymmetric compound in this category is one having an asymmetric atom attached to three other atoms, e.g., sulfur in thionylchlorofluoride (SOClF).

Note that the rapid inversion of the nitrogen pyramid in $NR_1R_2R_3$ amounts to racemization. It has not been possible to demonstrate optical activity in compounds containing asymmetric

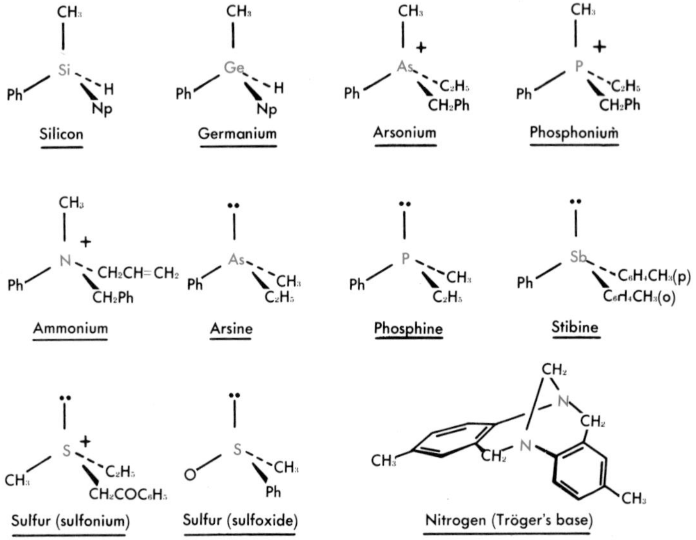

FIGURE 2–23

Examples of optically active and optically stable (at room temperature) compounds containing asymmetric atoms (marked in color) other than carbon (Np = α- naphthyl and Ph = phenyl). All compounds shown are asymmetric (C_1) except for Tröger's base (C_2).

nitrogen in which the inversion is structurally allowed. The inversion is structurally prohibited in Tröger's base (Figure 2–23).

When a constitutionally *unsymmetrical* acyclic molecule has n asymmetric atoms, $\frac{1}{2}(2^n)$ diastereomeric *dl* pairs or altogether 2^n stereoisomers may exist. Figure 2–24 shows the ephedrines as specific examples for $n = 2$ and also introduces the *Fischer convention* of projecting stereoisomers. According to this convention, the main chain of an acyclic stereoisomer, written vertically, is imagined in or below the plane of the paper, with the side chains, written horizontally, imagined projecting toward the observer. The convention ignores problems of conformation.

Constitutionally *symmetrical* molecules containing asymmetric atoms have fewer than 2^n stereoisomers: $2^{(n-1)} + 2^{(n-2)/2}$ when n is even and $2^{(n-1)}$ when n is odd. Among these isomers, the optically inactive diastereomers are designated by the prefix *meso* (see p. 81). For example, there are only three tartaric acids. As shown in Figure 2–25, two of these, the (+)- and (−)-isomers, are mixtures of conformational diastereomers. The *meso*-isomer

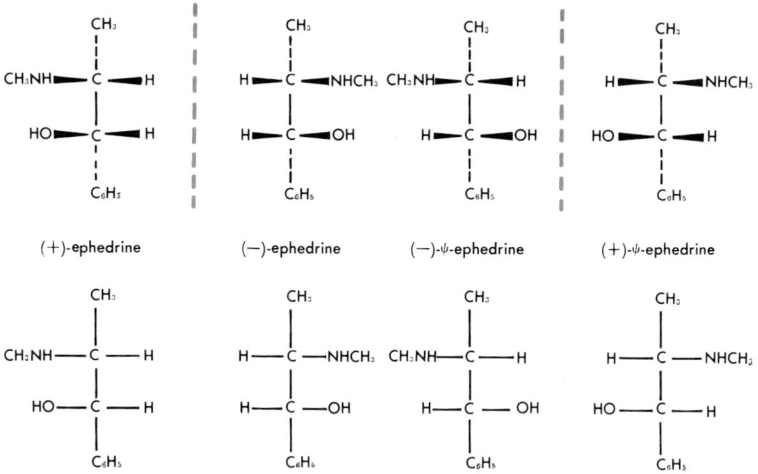

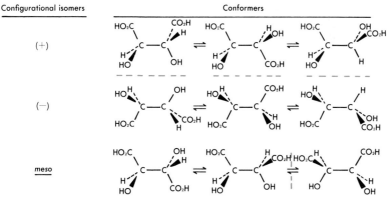

FIGURE 2–24

Examples of enantiomerism and diastereoisomerism in the ephedrines. Bottom, corresponding Fischer projections.

is a mixture of one symmetric (S_2) antiparallel and two interconvertible enantiomeric *gauche* (or syn-skew) conformers. As a result, the *meso*-isomer is optically inactive. It may be noted that the three stereoisomeric tartaric acids are also referred to as *configurational isomers* (see also p. 82).

FIGURE 2–25

Configurational and conformational isomerism in the tartaric acids. To simplify the analysis, effects of hydrogen bonding have been ignored.

When the four substituents on a carbon atom have the same group molecular formula but differ constitutionally, the carbon atom is still asymmetric. Thus $C(C_4H_9)_4$ has an asymmetric carbon atom if the four C_4H_9 groups are *n*-butyl, *sec*-butyl, isobutyl, and *t*-butyl. However, if two (or more) of the substituent groups have the same constitution and differ only stereoisomerically, the question of whether or not the central carbon atom is asymmetric may be more difficult to settle. This problem can be illustrated by the example of the four pentaric acids (Figure 2–26). This set of compounds consists of a *dl*-pair (*A*) and two *meso*-isomers (*B* and *C*). In each isomer the atoms C-2 and C-4 are clearly asymmetric, but there is some ambiguity about the terminology which should be used for C-3. Thus, in *A* (either enantiomer), if any two groups on C-3 are switched, the *same* isomer results; therefore, by our definition, C-3 is *not* an asymmetric carbon atom. Indeed, if the two -CHOHCOOH groupings are detached while keeping their configuration intact, it is seen that they are identical so that in that sense C-3 is not attached to two different groupings. This criterion (i.e., detaching the groups and examining them in *isolated* form) is equivalent to the criterion of exchange which we have adopted. However, as long as they remain an integral part of the molecule, the two groupings are *not* identical: The -CHOHCHOHCOOH groups attached to C-2 and to C-4 differ from each other stereochemically. Therefore, the presence of four different substituents on a carbon atom is not a sufficient condition (nor is it a necessary one; see exercise 2–14) for the presence of an asymmetric carbon atom.

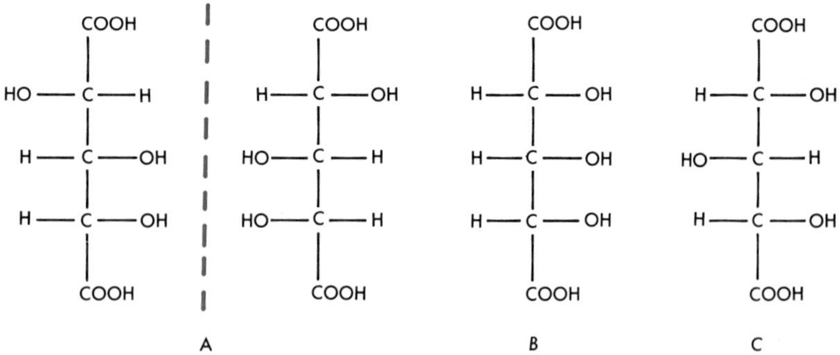

FIGURE 2–26

Configurational isomerism in the pentaric acids (Fischer projections).

In the case of the *meso*-pentaric acids, exchange of any two groups at C-3 *does* result in a new stereoisomer: *B* gives *C,* and vice versa. Examination of the -CHOHCOOH groupings in isolated form reveals in this case that they are not identical but are enantiomeric, and this condition persists even when C-2 and C-4 are considered as integral parts of the molecule. In *meso*-compounds of this sort, C-3 is clearly asymmetric by our definition, but, because the atom lies on a σ plane in the projection, this special case is sometimes referred to as a *pseudoasymmetric atom*.

The heptaric (pentahydroxypimelic) acids (Figure 2–27) are particularly instructive for they represent all the various stereochemical capabilities of a carbon atom containing two constitutionally identical substituents. The relevant atom in the heptaric acids is C-4. In asymmetric and optically active diastereomers *A–D,* the two groupings are related as *diastereomers* and C-4 is asymmetric. In asymmetric and optically active diastereomers *E* and *F,* the two groupings are *identical* (in isolated form); C-4 cannot be asymmetric since exchange of any two groups will not lead to a new stereoisomer. Finally, in nondissymmetric and optically inactive *meso*-forms *G–J,* C-4 is pseudoasymmetric since it is attached to two *enantiomeric* groupings.

The term *epimer* can also be clearly illustrated by reference to the heptaric acids. Among molecules containing asymmetric atoms, epimers are diastereomers which differ in the configuration of any *one* (and *only* one) of the several asymmetric atoms. The diastereomeric ephedrines and pentaric acids are necessarily epimeric. In the heptaric acids, *A* is epimeric with *C, E, F, G,* and *I*. In carbohydrate chemistry, the term has come to refer to the configuration at C-2 only, and epimers differing in configuration at C-1 are called *anomers*.

Among the variety of *meso*-compounds which contain asymmetric carbon atoms, two uncommon types deserve special mention because they illustrate some principles of general interest in stereochemistry. One type is illustrated by spirane B shown in Figure 1–18, a compound which is nondissymmetric, and therefore optically inactive, by virtue of the presence of a S_4 axis and despite the absence of a σ or a S_2 (i), elements which are more commonly encountered in nondissymmetric molecules. The second type is exemplified by the biphenyl shown in Figure 2–28. If the four blocking substituents (X) are large enough, a coplanar bi-

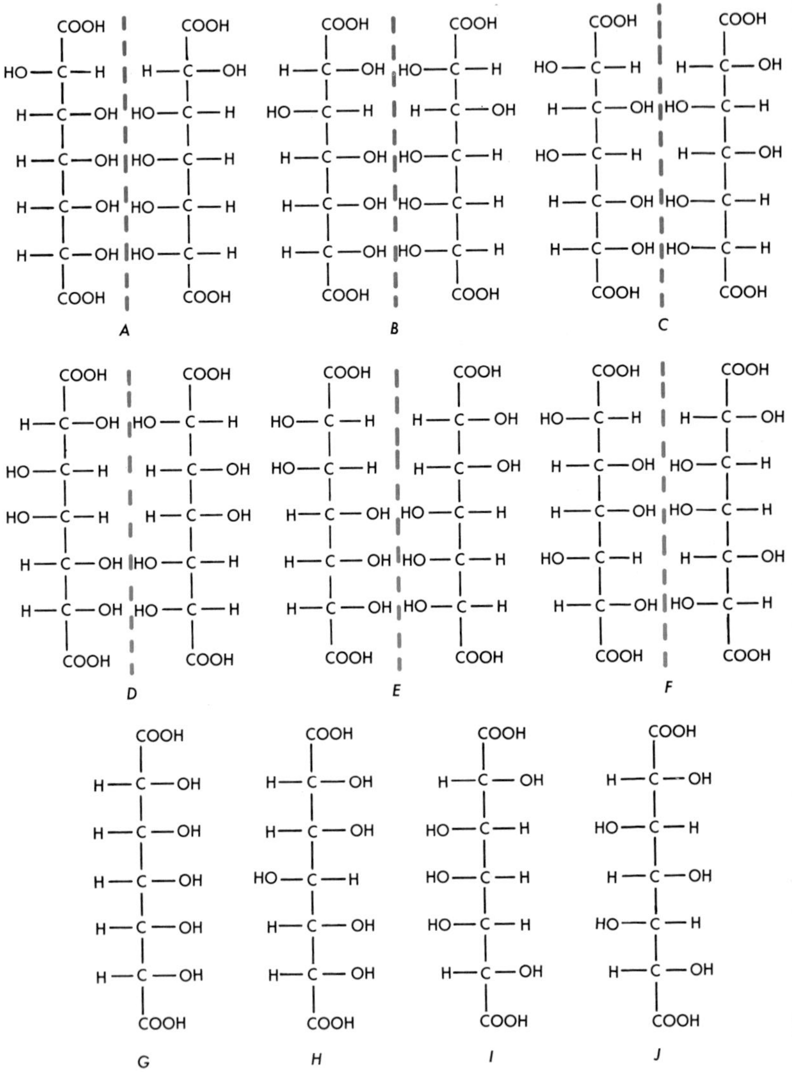

FIGURE 2-27

Configurational isomerism in the heptaric acids (Fischer projections).

phenyl conformation is ruled out. Under these circumstances the only nondissymmetric conformation of the biphenyl moiety is $\mathbf{D}_{2d}$, with σ planes intersecting at the pivot bond axis. At the same time, the only nondissymmetric conformations which are available to the two substituent groups -*Cabc* at the biphenyl 4,4′-positions (taken

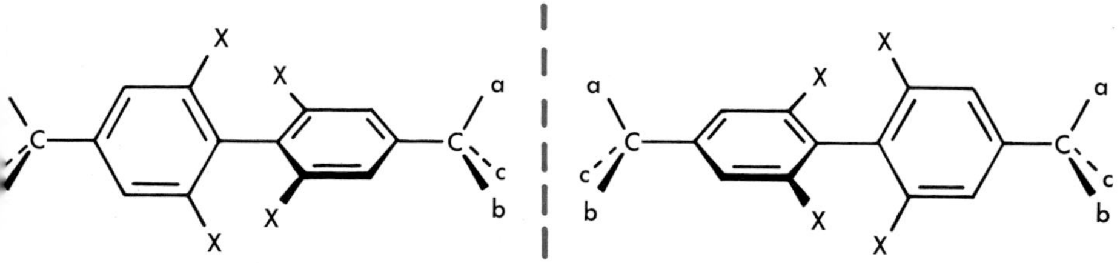

FIGURE 2–28

A meso-*compound containing only* C_1 *conformations.*

together as a unit) are (*a*) C_s with a σ plane *perpendicular* to the pivot bond axis (the arrangement shown in Figure 2–28), or (*b*) S_2 (cf., e.g., Figure 1–18), with S_2 coincident on the biphenyl pivot bond axis. Since D_{2d} is incompatible with either one of the last two conditions, it follows that the molecule is dissymmetric in all possible conformations and that the compound exists as a mixture of transient *dl*-pairs. However, these *dl*-pairs can interconvert by torsion around the bond to -*Cabc;* for example, either one of the enantiomeric conformations in Figure 2–28 can convert into the other by a 90° twist of both end-groups in the same direction. Since no conformations possessing reflection symmetry are available to the system, this example leads to the general conclusion that *racemization may proceed through intermediates or transition states which do not possess reflection symmetry.* In further illustration of our discussion in Section 2–2, this example also lends emphasis to the statement that molecular dissymmetry is a necessary but not a sufficient condition for optical activity.

We had earlier discussed (Section 2–4) the concept of dia-stereomeric protons and we now briefly return to this subject in the present context. A molecule containing asymmetric atoms and a methylene group generally shows two separate and distinct NMR signals for the two diastereomeric methylene protons, for example (Formula X):

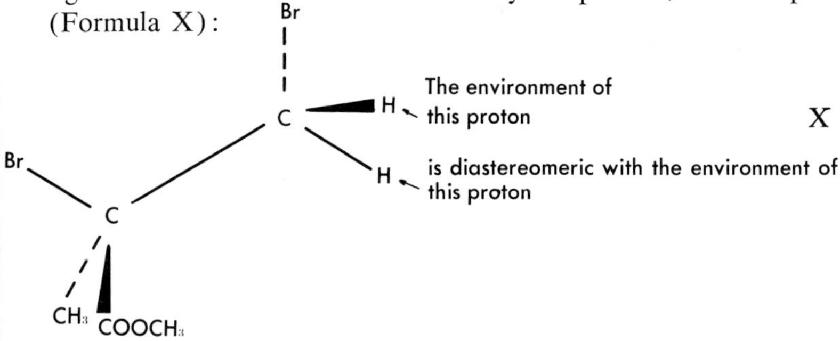

The diastereoisomerism of these protons is independent of conformation, and, no matter how rapid the rate of torsion around the central C—C bond, the environments of the two protons will always remain different, at any instant or on a time-average. Molecular dissymmetry is not a requirement for diastereoisomerism of the type discussed. For example, the protons (H_a and H_b) on each of the two methylene groups in diethyl acetal are diastereomeric (CH_3—CH_aH_b—$OCH(CH_3)O$—$CH_aH_bCH_3$). Note that the carbon atoms which carry diastereomeric protons are not asymmetric by our definition, yet they are attached to four different groups, in the sense that the protons are clearly distinguishable by a physical measurement (NMR). Such hydrogens even differ in reactivity (section 3–3)!

CONFIGURATIONAL NOTATIONS   In connection with the preceding discussion, we shall now briefly outline nomenclatures which serve to designate unequivocally the *absolute configuration* at an asymmetric atom. By absolute configuration we mean the description of the position or order of arrangement of the ligand atoms in space in relation to a commonly agreed upon macroscopic standard of chirality, e.g., a right-handed helix. For example, it is known that the absolute configuration of (+)-ephedrine is the one shown in Figure 2–24, rather than the mirror-image configuration (which corresponds to the (−)-isomer). The experimental basis for configurational assignments such as these will be discussed in section 3.

The simplest way to designate absolute configuration is to draw a picture of the molecule, indicating the relative positions of atoms in space. However, it is not always feasible to print or to communicate pictures and a shorthand notation is therefore required.

A precise and generally applicable notation is the following. The groups attached to the asymmetric atom are arranged according to a sequence rule in a priority order of decreasing atomic number and, for the same atomic number, decreasing isotopic mass. The lone pair in asymmetric sulfur atom and the like is considered a substituent and is given the lowest priority. If the atoms which are directly linked to the asymmetric atom are the same, priority order is determined by the nature of the atoms further away. Multiple linkages are treated formalistically as multiple single bonds, as for example in $C = O$, $C = N$, $C \equiv N$, $C = CH_2$

and phenyl which become $C\underset{CH}{\overset{O}{\diagup}}$, $C\underset{O}{\overset{N}{\diagup}}$, $C\underset{N}{\overset{N}{\diagdown}}N$, $C\underset{C}{\overset{CH_2}{\diagdown}}$ and $C{\overset{\diagup}{\diagdown}}CH$, respectively.

Thus, in order of decreasing priority:

Atoms: I, Br, Cl, F, O, N, C, H, lone pair

Isotopes: T, D, H

Groups: (a) $-C(CH_3)_3$, $-CH(CH_3)_2$, $-CH_2CH_3$, $-CH_3$

           (b) $-C(CH_3)_3$, $-CH(CH_3)CH_2CH_3$, $-CH_2CH(CH_3)_2$,

                                     $-CH_2(CH_2)_2CH_3$

           (c) $-COOCH_3$, $-COOH$, $-CONH_2$, $-COCH_3$, $-CHO$

           (d) $-C \equiv N$, $-C_6H_5$, $-C \equiv CH$, $-CH = CH_2$

The group of lowest priority is now viewed through a triangle formed by joining the other three. The triangle interposes itself between the observer and the group of lowest priority, which is viewed in a line with the bond axis joining it to the asymmetric atom. According to this conversion rule, if the observed order of decreasing priority of the three groups on the triangle is clockwise, the configuration is specified as (R), if counterclockwise it is (S). These symbols stand for *rectus* (right) and *sinister* (left), respectively. The example in Figure 2–29 shows the method applied to 2-butanol. Since the $(-)$-isomer is known to have the (R)-configuration, this compound is properly named $(-)-(R)$-2-butanol. The student should verify that all of the isomers shown in Figure 2–23 have the (R)-configuration, excepting Tröger's base

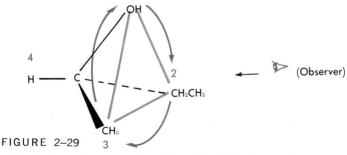

FIGURE 2–29

Designation of enantiomeric configurations, (R)-2-butanol.

in which both nitrogens have the (S)-configuration, and that $(+)$- and $(-)$-ephedrines and $(+)$- and $(-)$-ψ-ephedrines (Figure 2– 24) have the following configurations: $(1S: 2R)$, $(1R: 2S)$, $(1S: 2S)$, and $(1R: 2R)$, respectively (the carbon bearing the oxygen is C-1). Note that the prefixes *erythro* and *threo* are often employed to designate diastereomers such as these, according to whether like groups are on the same side or on opposite sides in the projection formula. Thus the ephedrines are *erythro-* and the ψ-ephedrines *threo*-isomers.

Some optically active compounds are grouped in families whose members are closely related. For example, the α-amino acids (RCHNH₂COOH) which are found in higher living organisms can all be represented by the Fischer projection formula shown (Formula XI):

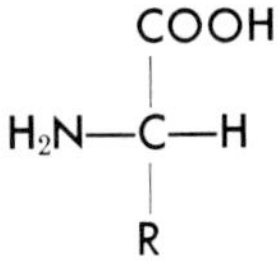

$$
\begin{array}{c}
\text{COOH} \\
|\\
\text{H}_2\text{N—C—H} \qquad\qquad \text{XI} \\
|\\
\text{R}
\end{array}
$$

For convenience, this particular configuration is arbitrarily designated by the prefix L$_s$ (or simply L), where the subscript refers to the standard in the series, $(-)$-serine (R=CH₂OH). The enantiomers are prefixed by D$_s$ (or simply D). Members in each family have *corresponding configurations*. The statement that they have the *same* configurations might imply that members of the same family all have the (R)- or (S)-configuration and this is not necessarily true. Thus, members of the L-family usually have the (S)-configuration, but there are exceptions: L-cysteine (R=CH₂SH) has the (R)-configuration.

Similarly, α-hydroxy acids which have the projection formula shown below are arbitrarily designated by the prefix D$_g$ (or D), where the subscript refers to the standard in the series, $(+)$-glyceraldehyde, also shown below (Formula XII):

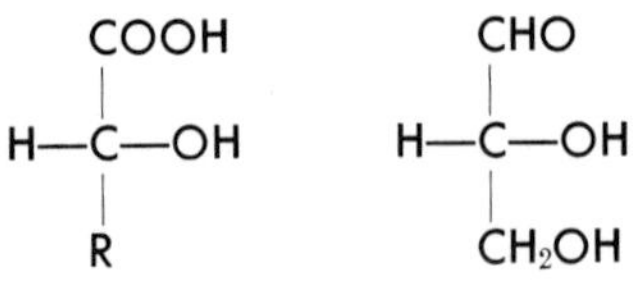

$$
\begin{array}{cc}
\text{COOH} & \text{CHO} \\
| & | \\
\text{H—C—OH} & \text{H—C—OH} \qquad \text{XII}\\
| & | \\
\text{R} & \text{CH}_2\text{OH}
\end{array}
$$

The configurational notations D and L must never be confused with the rotational prefixes *d* and *l*, to which they bear no immediate relationship.

2–6   Torsional Stereoisomerism in the Presence of Asymmetric Atoms

The features of atomic asymmetry and restricted rotation around single or double bonds may be combined in the same molecule. For example, there are four stereoisomers of 4-methyl-2-hexene, i.e., two diastereomeric *dl*-pairs. In compounds of this sort, torsion around the double bond interconverts diastereomers but not enantiomers, whereas inversion of the configuration at the asymmetric carbon atom interconverts enantiomers but does not interconvert diastereomers unless other asymmetric atoms are also present. In a compound such as hepta-2,5-dien-4-ol, the central carbon atom C-4 is asymmetric only when the two double bonds have different configurations: The two substituents are then diastereomerically related in analogy with heptaric acids *A-D* (Figure 2–27). There are four stereoisomers of this compound, one *dl*-pair and two *meso* forms.

Combination of atomic asymmetry and conformational isomerism is implicit in all but the simplest structures containing asymmetric carbon, as indicated in the example of the tartaric acids (Figure 2–25). This combination assumes particular importance in the stereochemical analysis of cyclohexane ring systems, as illustrated in Figure 2–30 for disubstituted cyclohexanes in which the substituents are identical. Note that the *cis*-1,2-isomer exists as a conformational *dl*-pair, that the 1,1-, *trans*-1,3- and *cis*-1,4-isomers suffer degenerate interconversions, and that the *trans*-1,2-, *cis*-1,3-, and *trans*-1,4-isomers exist as mixtures of conformational diastereomers. The conformational interconversions are exceedingly rapid at room temperature. This conclusion derives from the observation that in cases of degenerate interconversions the NMR signal of fluorine atoms or methyl protons in 1,1-difluoro- or 1,1-dimethyl cyclohexanes at room temperature consists of a single signal (apart from spin-spin coupling); cf. p. 77.

This analysis may be extended to the fused cyclohexanes exemplified by decalin, perhydrophenanthrene, perhydroanthacene, and the steroids. Decalins can exist in diastereomeric *cis*-

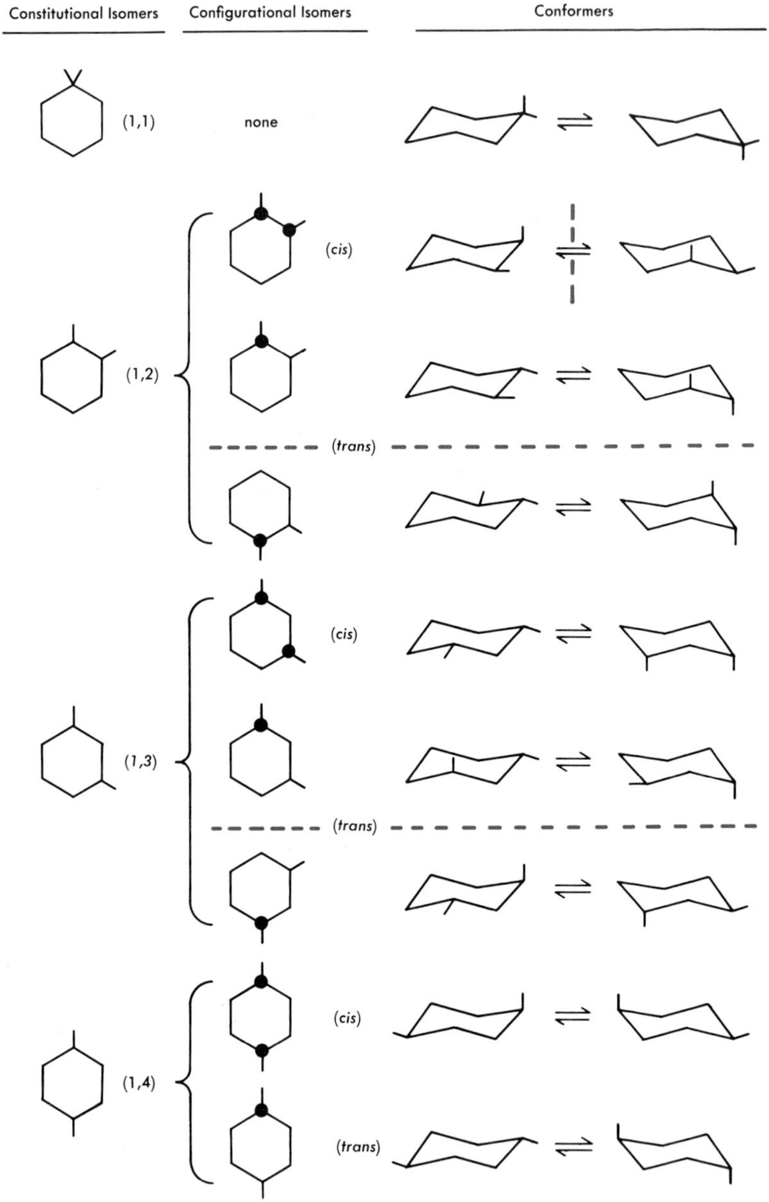

FIGURE 2–30

Stereoisomerism in cyclohexane substituted by two identical groups (e.g., dimethylcyclohexane). The heavy dot indicates a hydrogen atom projecting toward the observer.

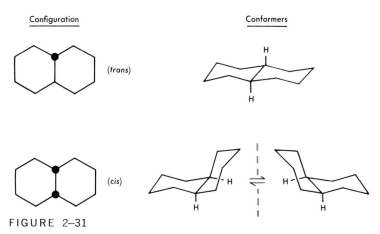

Configuration   Conformers

(trans)

(cis)

FIGURE 2–31

Stereoisomerism in the decalins.

and *trans*-forms (Figure 2–31). The *trans*-system is locked, but two enantiomeric *cis*- conformers (C_2) are possible which interconvert through flexible forms. It follows that the disposition (*a* or *e*) of a substituent in the 1- or 2-position of decalin remains unaltered only in the *trans*-isomer, but that for the *cis*- isomer two diastereomeric conformers are possible, differing in the disposition of the substituent. More complex systems may be illustrated with the perhydrophenanthrenes. As seen in Figure 2–32, there are ten stereoisomers (two *meso* forms and four *dl*-pairs). The nomenclature refers to the bonding arrangements around the central cyclohexane ring and is self-explanatory. For the *cis-syn-trans-, cis-anti-trans-,* and *trans-anti-trans-* configurations there is no conformational isomerism. The *cis-syn-cis*-isomer exists in the form of a conformational *dl*-pair reminiscent of *cis*-1,2-dimethylcyclohexane. Each configurational enantiomer of the *cis-anti-cis*-form exists as a mixture of two diastereomeric conformers, reminiscent of *trans*-1,2-dimethylcyclohexane. The *trans-syn-trans*-isomer is the highest energy form in this series, since the central ring necessarily assumes the boat conformation: In order to remain all-chair, the isomer would have to have the *aa-ae-ee* conformation, but a chair ring cannot be fused to an *aa*-junction.

While *cis-trans* isomerism is observed in the bicyclo[4.4.0]-ring systems illustrated in the preceding paragraph, isomerism cannot occur in some smaller ring systems where the strain of bridging the *trans*-positions of one ring by the other is prohibitive.

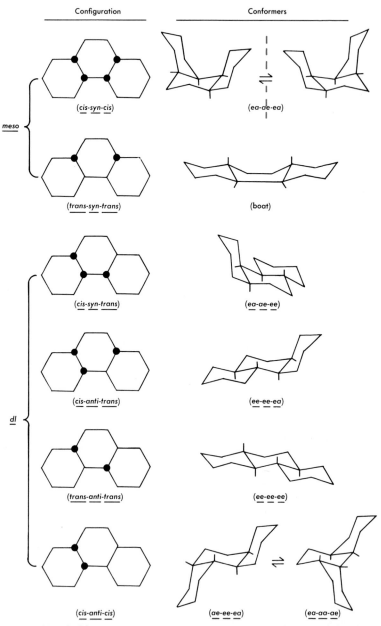

FIGURE 2–32

Stereoisomerism in the perhydrophenanthrenes. Only one enantiomer of each dl-pair is shown.

WEST HILLS COLLEGE LIBRARY
COALINGA, CALIFORNIA

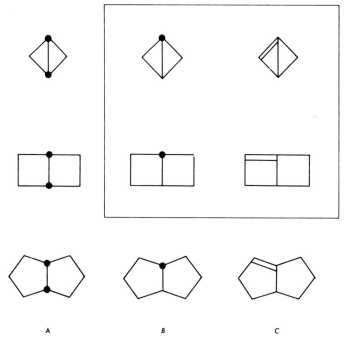

A   **B**   **C**

FIGURE 2–33

Some stereochemical relationships in simple fused bicyclic ring systems.
A, cis-fused; B, trans-fused; C, double bond at bridgehead. Boxed compounds are highly strained and have not yet been prepared.

In Figure 2–33 are shown *cis-* and *trans-*fused bicyclo[1.1.0]butanes, bicyclo[2.2.0]hexanes, bicyclo[3.3.0]octanes, and corresponding olefins. The *cis*-fused form is comparatively stable in all three systems. The instability of the *trans*-form is seen to go hand-in-hand with the instability of the bridgehead olefin in all cases, and for the same reason, *viz.*, the requirement of intolerable bond angle deformation. This analogy can be extended to small bicyclic systems containing three carbon bridges (instead of only two), as illustrated by *nor*camphor or Tröger's base. Although *nor*camphor has two asymmetric carbon atoms, the stereoisomeric possibilities are restricted to the two enantiomers which have the bridgehead hydrogens on the outside of the ring system (Figure 2–34*A*). Any diastereomer *B* would be exceedingly unstable as the result of intolerable bond angle deformation and nonbonded compressions. In the related olefins *C,* the source of the instability is prohibitive torsional strain around the double bond (Bredt's rule).

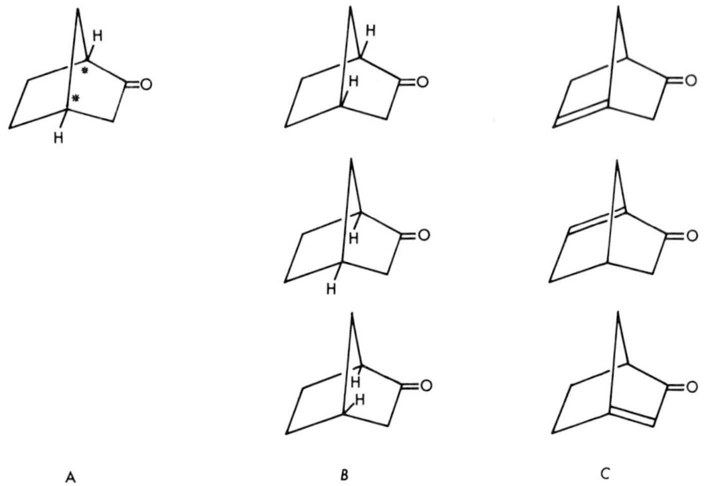

FIGURE 2–34

(+)-Nor*camphor* (A) *with asymmetric atoms starred;* B, *the "impossible" diastereomers;* C, *some of the "forbidden" bridgehead olefins. The only other stable form of* nor*camphor is the enantiomer of* A.

The structural restrictions which we have just enumerated are relaxed as soon as one of the rings becomes large enough to accommodate whatever functionalities need to be incorporated. Thus, there is no reason why both *cis-* and *trans*-bicyclo[10.1.0]undecane should not exist, why a double bond should not be formed at the bridgehead of bicyclo[4.4.1]undecane, or why there should not exist four diastereomeric *dl*-pairs of bicyclo[12.12.1]heptacosan-2-one, the "expanded" analog of *nor*camphor.

2–7   Macromolecules

Stereoisomerism in polymeric molecules presents problems of special interest which will be discussed in this section.

Consider the head-to-tail polymerization (Eq. 2–5) of α-olefins (vinyl polymerization):

$$n(CH_2 = CHR) \rightarrow -CH_2CHR\text{-}(CH_2CHR)_{n-2}\text{-}CH_2CHR\text{-} \tag{2-5}$$

In the resulting poly-α-olefin, the lateral or branch groups R on the main or backbone chain are attached to carbon atoms which are asymmetric in the sense of our definition (Section 1–4). In further discussing the stereochemistry of such polymers it is convenient and quite legitimate to assume that the polymer chain is of indefinite length and that the terminal sections are at a considerable distance along the main chain from the nonterminal section under consideration. We shall adopt this approximation in subsequent discussions.

The process of polymerization of α-olefins may be schematized as shown in Figure 2–35, i.e., as a sequence of *trans*-additions. The stereochemical capabilities of such additions are in essence limited only by the number of monomer units which combine, but, in the main, four categories of diastereomeric polymers may be distinguished. In *A* the *trans*-addition is perfectly stereoregular or *tactic,* and the *R*-groups in the resulting polymer are all on the same side. A local σ plane passes through each asymmetric carbon atom

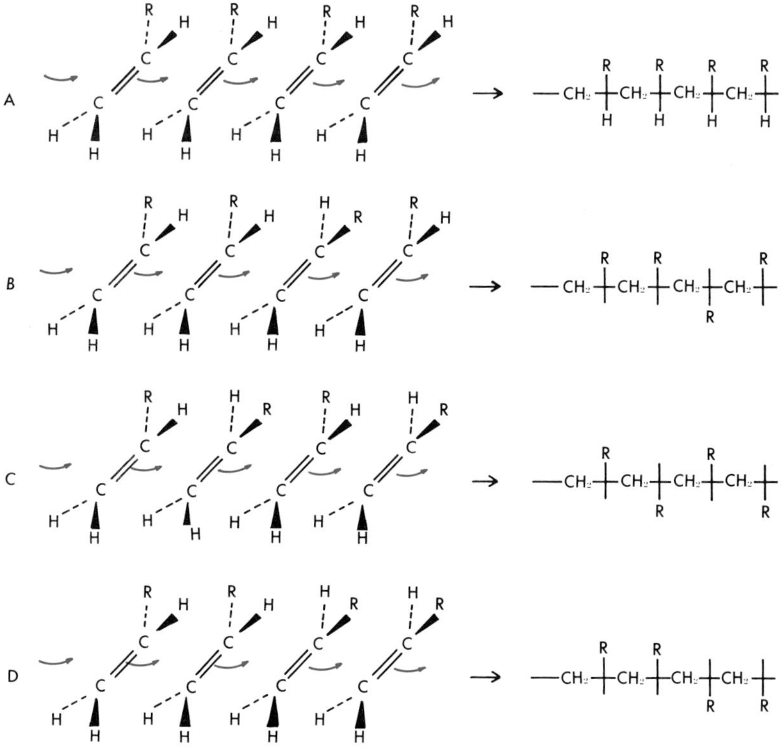

FIGURE 2–35

Segments of diastereomeric poly-α-olefins. A, isotactic; B, atactic; C, syndiotactic; D, stereoblock. Fischer projections are shown on the right. The colored arrows indicate the direction of transaddition-polymerization.

which is therefore pseudoasymmetric; in fact, *A* may be regarded as an extension in type of heptaric acid *G* (Figure 2–27). If priority is given arbitrarily to one end of the chain as opposed to the other, all the asymmetric carbon atoms are seen to have the (*R*) configuration; if the priority order is reversed, all the asymmetric carbon atoms have the (*S*)-configuration. Thus, although the specification of (*R*) or (*S*) cannot be directly applied to these pseudoasymmetric atoms, it is seen that they all have the same configuration. Using D and L to designate configuration in these cases, we may summarize the stereochemistry of polymer *A* by (. . . . DDDDDD . . .) or (. . . LLLLLL . .). Such polymers are called *isotactic*.

If the positions of *R* and *H* are reversed at irregular intervals, as shown in *B* of Figure 2–35, the stereoregularity or *tacticity* of the polymer is destroyed; segments of such *atactic* polymers might be symbolized by (. . . DLDDDD . . .) or (. . . DLDLLD . . .). If, however, the positions of *R* and *H* are alternately reversed, as shown in *C* of Figure 2–35, the polymer is again tactic. Such polymers, in which the stereochemistry is (. . . DLDLDL . . .), are called *syndiotactic*. The asymmetric carbon atoms are again pseudoasymmetric, and a syndiotactic polymer may be regarded as an extension in type of heptaric acid J (Figure 2–27). Note that the methylene protons of isotactic polymers

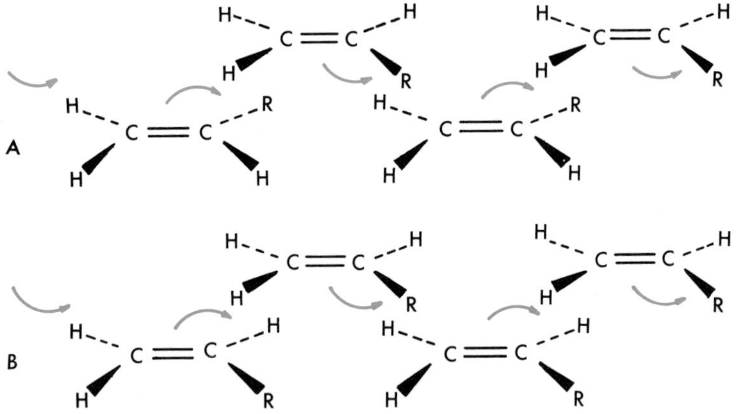

FIGURE 2–36

A mechanistic alternative to the trans-*polymerization shown in Figure 2–35. Cis- opening of the α-olefin leads to isotactic (A) or syndiotactic (B) polymers as shown.*

are diastereomeric whereas those of syndiotactic polymers are enantiomeric.

Often the polymer consists of isotactic sections differing in the configuration of the chain sequences, as shown in *D* of Figure 2–35. Such *stereoblock* polymers might be symbolized by (. . DDDDDLLLLDDD . . . .).

The various stereoisomeric poly-α-olefins discussed above may alternatively be generated by a *cis-* rather than by a *trans*-addition mechanism, provided only that the presentation of the olefin in the polymerization sequence is reversed, as shown by a comparison of Figures 2–35 and 2–36. There is evidence pointing to the *cis*-addition as the preferred mechanism of polymerization, but the student should be conversant with the stereochemical consequences of both modes of addition polymerization.

We have learned that diastereomers show pronounced differences in physical properties, and this is also true of the diastereomeric polymers. Familiar examples are starch (poly-α-D-glucopyranoside) and cellulose (poly-β-D-glucopyranoside), which differ only in the configuration of the linkages between identical monomeric constituent units. Similarly, the 1,4-polymerization of isoprene may give rise to gutta-percha (*trans*-linkages) or Hevea rubber (*cis*-linkages) (Formula XIII):

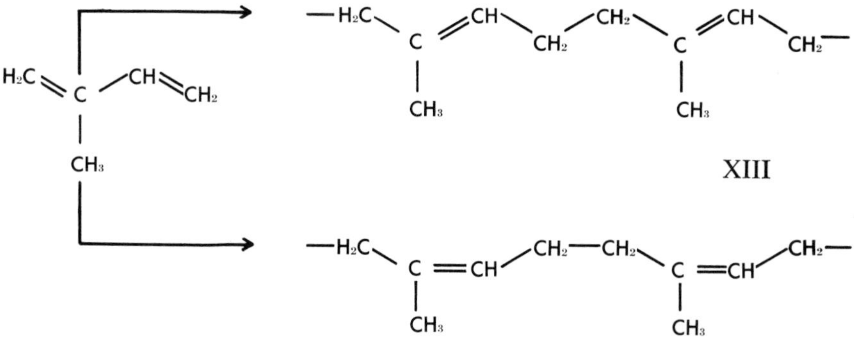

XIII

In general, an increase in tacticity is accompanied by a marked increase in crystallinity. Thus isotactic polymers are often brittle, high-melting solids, whereas the corresponding atactic polymers are rubbery or low-melting solids, or even sirupy liquids.

When the monomer is dissymmetric and optically active, the

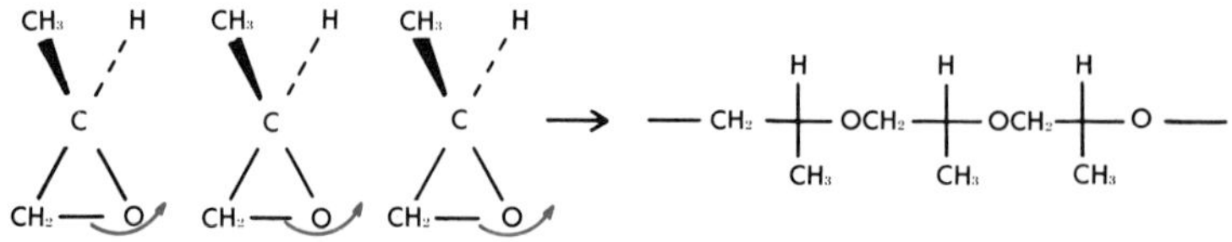

FIGURE 2–37

Polymerization of (R)-propylene oxide.

polymer is likewise. The polymerization of optically active (*R*)-propylene oxide leads to optically active poly-(*R*)-propylene oxide (Figure 2–37). In this isotactic polymer each tertiary carbon atom is asymmetric and not pseudoasymmetric. The biopolymers, i.e., the polysaccharides (such as starch and cellulose), polypeptides, proteins, polynucleotides, and nucleic acids are all dissymmetric and optically active since their constituent units, i.e., the simple saccharides and α-amino acids, are dissymmetric and optically active; they also have corresponding configurations.

One of the most interesting features of macromolecules is their *secondary structure*. This term refers to the conformation or coil of the main chain, whereas *primary structure* defines the constitution of the polymer and the configuration of the asymmetric carbons along the backbone or in the side chains. Even if the primary structure contains no dissymmetric groupings, the secondary structure may still be arranged in the form of a helix and an element of dissymmetry may thus be introduced. For instance, the chains in teflon (. . . $CF_2CF_2CF_2CF_2$ . . .) are twisted so that a full turn is executed every 26 CF_2-units. The polymer molecules exist in this case as interconvertible (through torsion about carbon-carbon single bonds) right- and left-handed helices. Similarly, tactic, especially isotactic, polymers have secondary structures in which the main chain assumes a helical conformation (Figure 2–38).

If the primary structure does contain dissymmetric groupings, the twist of the helix introduces an additional element of dissymmetry and with it the possibility of diastereoisomerism. This is illustrated for the case of a polypeptide α-helix in Figure 2–39. Close examination of the models confirms that the lateral nonbonded interactions between the various groupings in contiguous coils of the helix cannot be the same for the two diastereomers. As the result of the difference in free energy of the diastereomers,

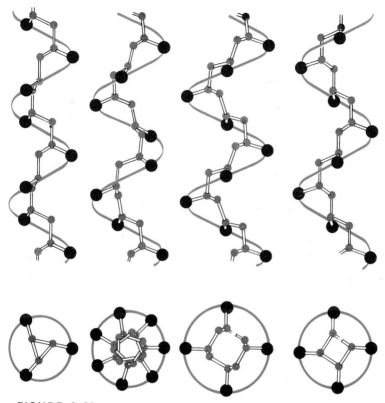

FIGURE 2–38

Helical forms assumed by some isotactic chains in the crystalline state. Only one enantiomer is shown. The large black spheres represent alkyl or aryl groupings.

one of the enantiomeric helices will predominate in the equilibrium *dextro*-helix ⇌ random coil ⇌ *levo*-helix. If, in the case of the poly-L-α-amino acid α-helix, the predominant isomer is the right-handed form, it follows necessarily that the predominant isomer of the poly-D-α-amino acid α-helix must be left-handed form, since enantiomers have identical free energies. In short, the dissymmetry of the monomer induces a preferential chirality in the main chain. This is further illustrated in the case of the DNA double helix (Figure 2–40). Each of the two polynucleotide chains has dissymmetric D-2-deoxyribose units built into the primary structure, and the absolute configuration of this sugar determines the

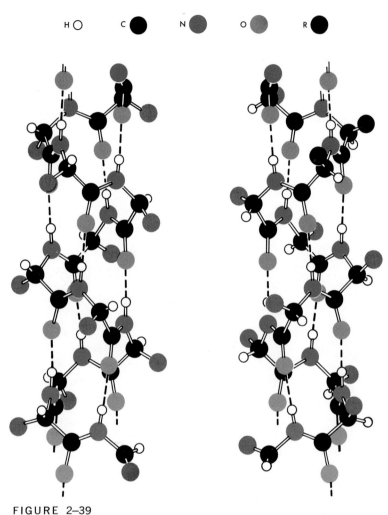

FIGURE 2–39

*Left-handed (on the left) and right-handed (on the right) forms of the poly-*L*-α-amino acid α-helix. The broken lines indicate hydrogen bonds.*

absolute chirality of the two-stranded complex helix, which is right-handed as shown.

The optical rotatory power of macromolecules in which the primary structure contains dissymmetric units is made up of two components: the so-called *residue rotation* of the dissymmetric

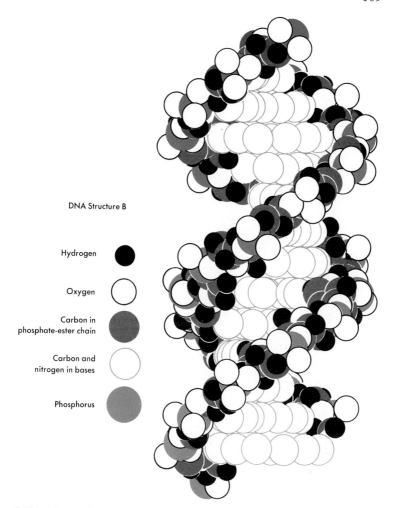

DNA Structure B

Hydrogen

Oxygen

Carbon in
phosphate-ester chain

Carbon and
nitrogen in bases

Phosphorus

FIGURE 2–40

*Deoxyribonucleic acid (DNA). The purines and pyrimidines are piled
along the major axis.*

units, which could persist even in a randomly coiled main chain,
and the rotational contribution of the helical conformation, e.g.,
of α-helical polyglycine in the case of polypeptides. Since the two
types of contribution give rise to separate and distinct electronic
transitions, it often becomes possible to gauge the relative importance of the two effects on the total rotation by a study of the ORD

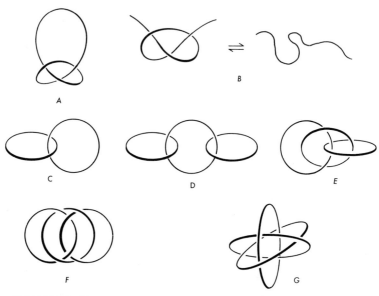

FIGURE 2–41

A, *trefoil;* B, *open knot;* C, *two-ring catenane;* D–G, *three-ring catenanes.*
Only one of the enantiomers of A, B, E *and* F *is shown.*

or CD. Helical polypeptides and certain isotactic poly-α-olefins which contain asymmetric carbons in the lateral chains sometimes exhibit an unusually high optical rotation: This is the effect which results from the contribution of the secondary structure to the total optical rotatory power, a contribution which is absent when the main chain is randomly coiled.

2–8   Topological Isomerism

Cyclic molecules are capable of another type of structural isomerism which has been termed *topological isomerism.* This may be exemplified (Figure 2–41) by knots, such as the trefoil *A,* and by interlocking rings (*catenanes*), such as *C-G.* Since this isomerism implies different arrangements of atoms in space, it may be appropriately considered another type of stereoisomerism.

Models indicate that a knotted cycloparaffin of topology *A* may be formed from a chain containing fifty carbon atoms or more. The knotted loop $C_{50}H_{100}$ is a topological isomer of the unknotted cycloparaffin $C_{50}H_{100}$, and the two isomers cannot be interconverted without breaking a carbon-carbon bond. In contrast, the open knot (Figure 2–41*B*) is merely another conformation of the acyclic unknotted paraffin. No trefoil has yet been rationally synthesized. However, in the closure of very large and presumably unknotted rings, a minute probability exists that knotted loops are also formed at the same time and that these are present as exceedingly minor and as yet undetected impurities accompanying the unknotted loops.

Catenanes, as models indicate, may be formed from somewhat smaller chains (twenty to thirty carbon atoms). The synthesis of a two-ring 34,34-catenane has been accomplished by the closure of a 34-ring through preformed cyclotetratriacontane. The yields in this closure are very low because the probability is small that threading of a chain through a ring will occur faster than closure (Formula XIV):

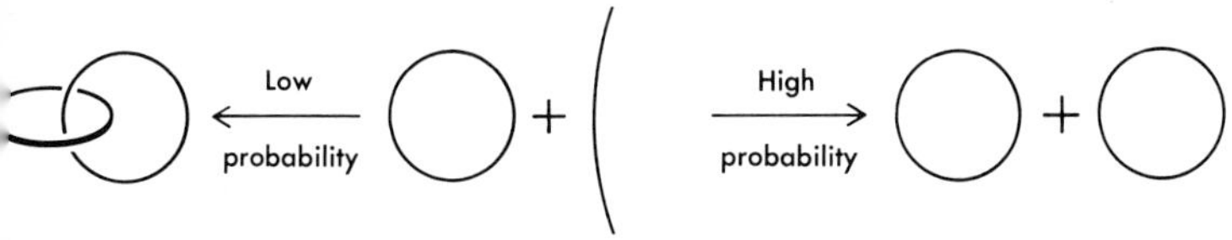

Although catenanes are composed of independent molecular subunits, they are single molecules in the sense that the combination of interlocking rings persists in solution and survives molecular collisions.

The complexity of topological isomerism in catenanes increases with an increase in the number of subcycles. A three-ring catenane may exist in four isomeric forms *D-G*, two of which (*E* and *F*) are *dl*-pairs and may therefore exhibit optical activity.

2–9   Exercises

2–1   A number of structures are shown below. For each one, list the possible stereoisomers (ignoring conformational isomerism), indicate the diastereomeric or enantiomeric relationships, and mark any *optical isomers* (stereoisomers which are optically active regardless of whether their relationship to other stereoisomers is enantiomeric or diastereomeric).

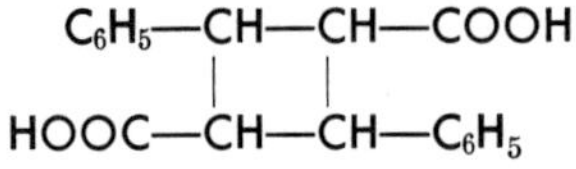

C₆H₅—CH—CH—COOH
HOOC—CH—CH—C₆H₅

A. Truxillic acid

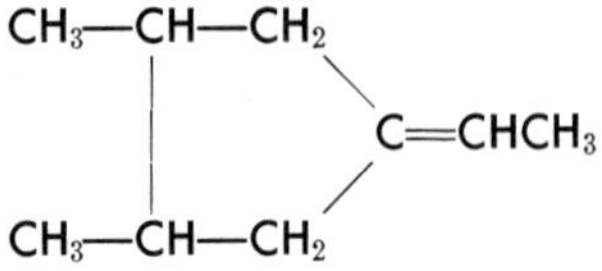

CH₃—CH—CH₂
CH₃—CH—CH₂ ⟩C=CHCH₃

B.

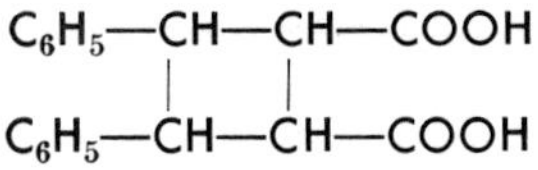

C₆H₅—CH—CH—COOH
C₆H₅—CH—CH—COOH

C. Truxinic acid

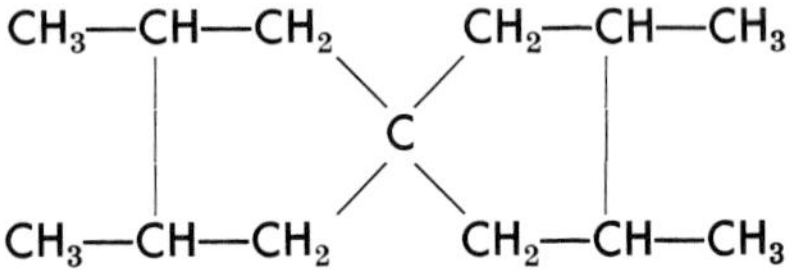

CH₃—CH—CH₂   CH₂—CH—CH₃
            C
CH₃—CH—CH₂   CH₂—CH—CH₃

D.

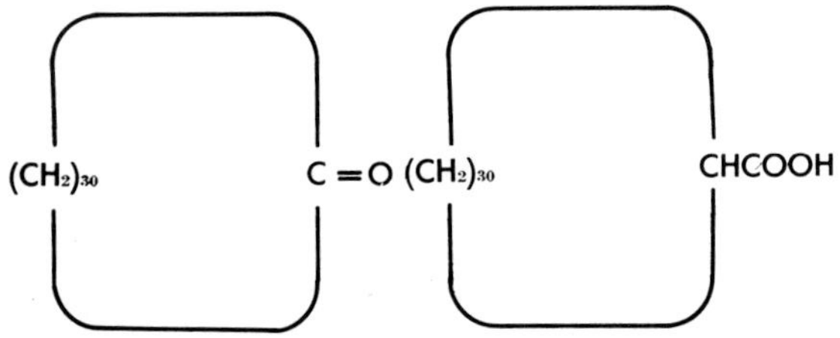

(CH₂)₃₀   C=O   (CH₂)₃₀   CHCOOH

a   b

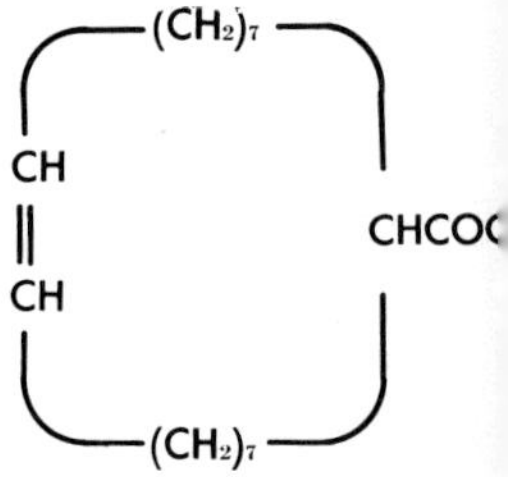

—(CH₂)₇—
CH
‖
CH
—(CH₂)₇—

CHCOO

F.

E. Two-ring catenanes
a-a, *a-b*, and *b-b*

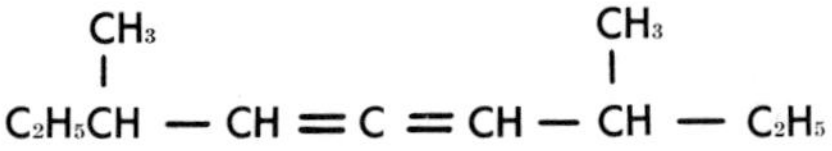

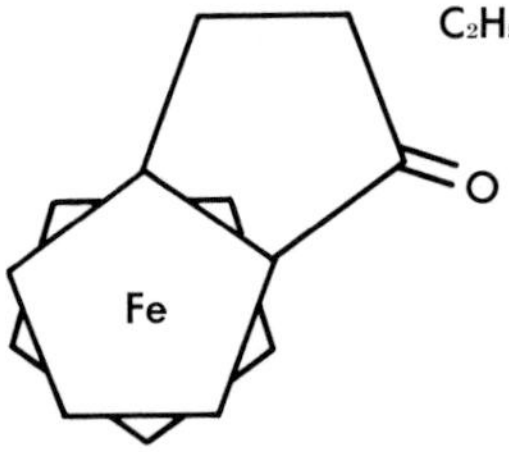

G. An example of
ferrocene dissymmetry

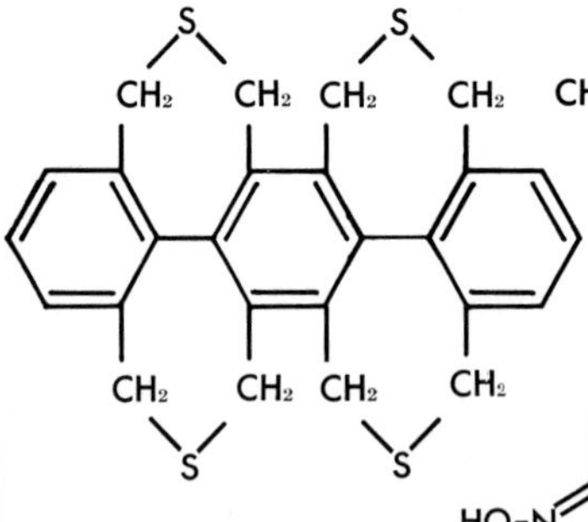

Fe
O

CH₃
|
C₂H₅CH — CH = C = CH — CH — C₂H₅
                              |
                             CH₃

H.

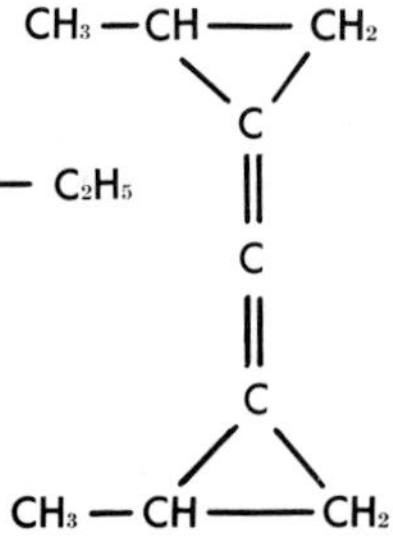

CH₃ —CH— CH₂
        C
        ‖
        C
        ‖
        C
CH₃ —CH— CH₂

I.

S   S
\   \
CH₂   CH₂ CH₂   CH₂

CH₂   CH₂ CH₂   CH₂
/   /
S   S

K.

J.

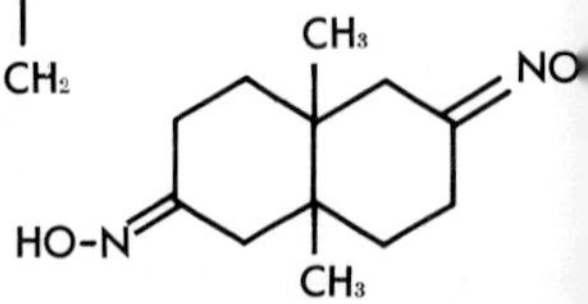

CH₃
|
     NO
HO-N=
        |
       CH₃

L.

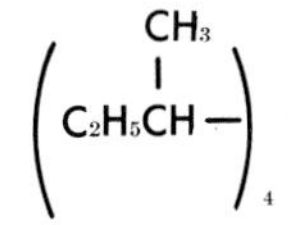

$$\left(\begin{array}{c} CH_3 \\ | \\ C_2H_5CH - \end{array} \right)_4 C$$

M.

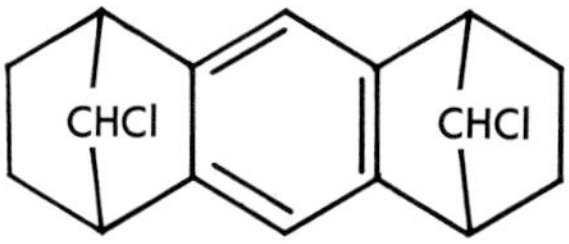

N.

$[CH_2CHDCD_2]_4$

O.

Tetrachlorocubane
(all constitutional isomers)

P.

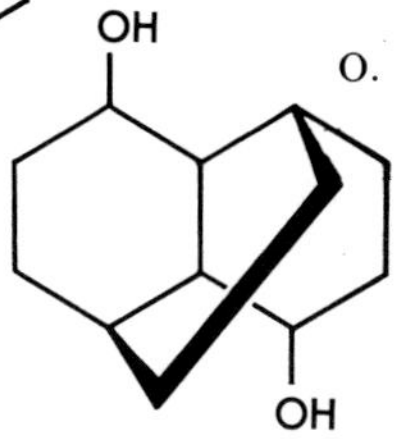

Q. (chair only).

2–2   Dicarbene C_3 ($C=C=C$) adds two molecules of propylene to give a mixture of three diastereomers of I (Exercise 2-1) in the ratio $1:1:2$. Identify the last diastereomer.

2–3   "Optical isomers absorb at the same wave length in the UV, but their extinction coefficients may differ appreciably when their spectra are measured with circularly polarized light." Is the preceding statement true when "optical isomers" refers to "enantiomers," or to "optically active diastereomers," or to both?

2–4   Classify the methylene protons attached to the benzyl or substituted benzyl carbon atoms in the following compounds according to their type of stereochemical nonequivalence as (*a*) enantiomeric, (*b*) diastereomeric.

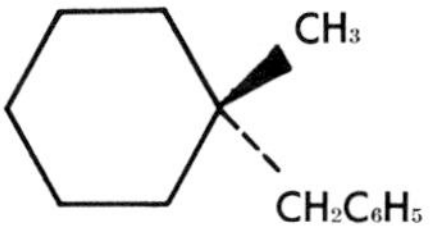

A.

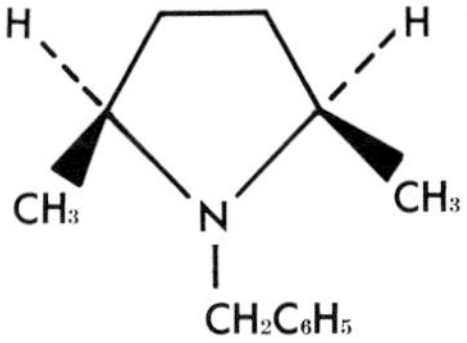

B.

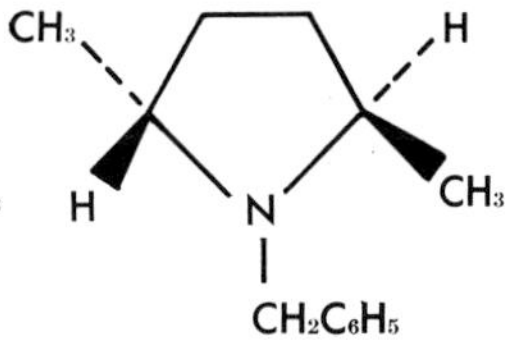

C.

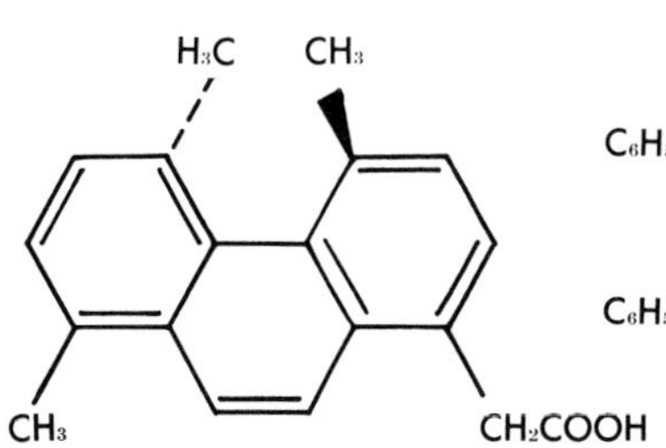

D.

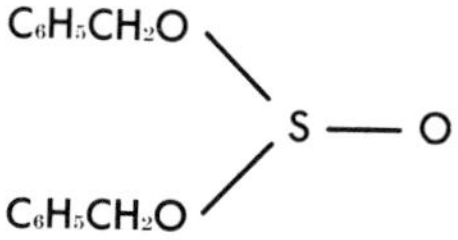

E.

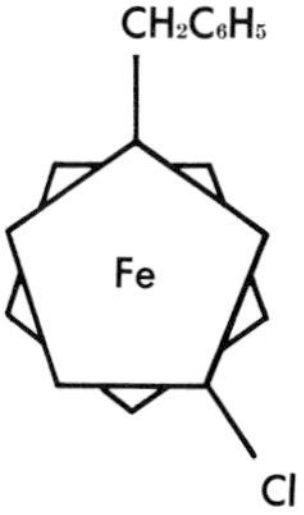

F.

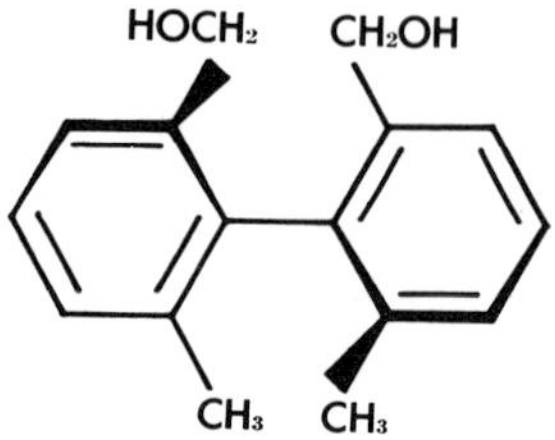

G. 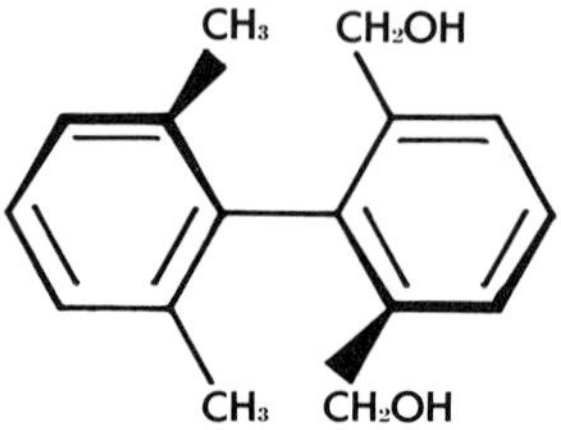   H. 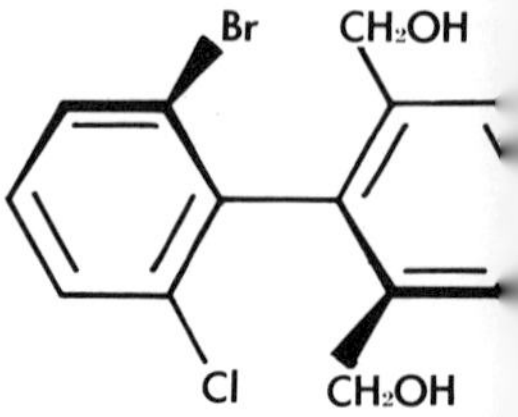   I.

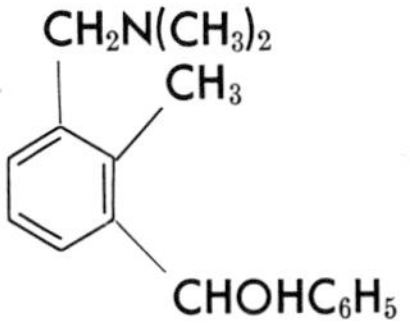

J. 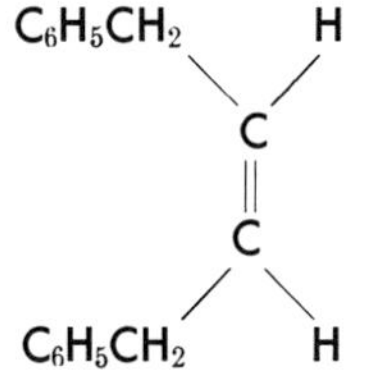   K. 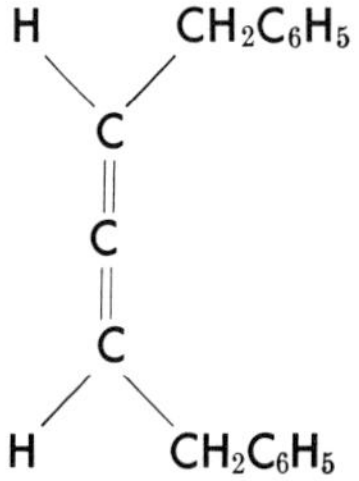   L.

2–5   (*a*) Identify the constitutions of $C_4H_{10}O$ (optically active), C_4H_8 (two stereoisomers), C_5H_{10} (optically active).

(*b*) RCOOH $\xrightarrow{H_2/Pt}$ Product.   Identify R for the following cases:

RCOOH	Product
(i) $C_5H_6O_2$, optically active	$C_5H_8O_2$, opt. inactive, nonresolvable
(ii) $C_5H_6O_2$, optically active	$C_5H_{10}O_2$, opt. inactive, nonresolvable
(iii) $C_6H_8O_2$, optically active	$C_6H_{12}O_2$, opt. inactive, nonresolvable
(iv) $C_5H_8O_2$, two nonresolvable forms	$C_5H_{10}O_2$, nonresolvable
(v) $C_5H_8O_2$, two nonresolvable forms	$C_5H_{10}O_2$, resolvable
(vi) $C_5H_8O_2$, optically active	$C_5H_{10}O_2$, optically active
(vii) $C_5H_8O_2$, one nonresolvable form	$C_5H_{10}O_2$, resolvable

(resolvable = separable into enantiomeric forms)

2–6   The half-lives of racemization of NO$_2$-substituted 2-nitro-6-carboxy-2'-methoxybiphenyls at 25° are: 3', 1905 min.; 5', 35 min. Suggest an explanation.

2–7   The optical rotation of the anhydride shown below (a single stereoisomer) rapidly falls to zero on standing in an inert solvent. Are the relative configurations at the two asymmetric carbon atoms the same or are they opposite?

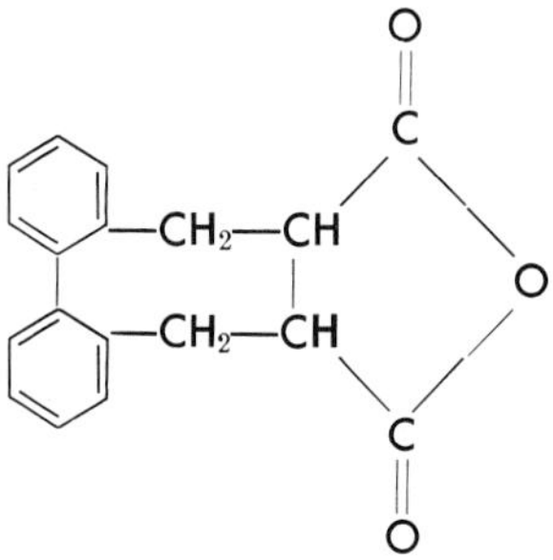

2–8   Of the following diastereomers of inositol (1,2,3,4,5,6-hexahydroxycyclohexane):

   (*a*) the *allo*-isomer exists in solution as a nonresolvable *dl*-pair,
   (*b*) the *dl*-isomer is the only resolvable diastereomer, and
   (*c*) both *cis*- and *muco*-isomers exist in solution in a single chair conformation.

Assign configurations to the inositols which are consistent with the given information.

2–9   Describe in detail the stereoisomeric perhydroanthracenes, employing the format of Figure 2–32, p. 100.

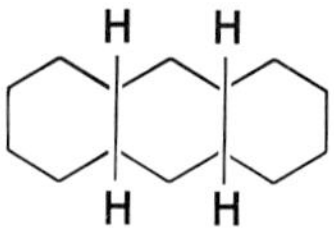

2–10   Describe the stereochemical relationships among the stereoisomers of ricinoleic acid.

$$CH_3(CH_2)_5-CHOH-CH_2-CH=CH-(CH_2)_7COOH$$

2–11   How would the number and types of isomers in Figure 2–30 be affected if the two substituents were not identical (e.g., methylethylcyclohexane)?

2–12   Sphingosine (*A*), sulforaphene (*B*), mycomycin (*C*), and nemotinic acid (*D*) are naturally occurring substances. How many stereoisomers are there for each?

$$CH_3—(CH_2)_{13}—CH=CH—CHOH—CHNH_2—CH_2OH$$

(*A*)

$$CH_3—SO—CH=CH—(CH_2)_2—NCS$$

(*B*)

$$HC\equiv C—C\equiv C—CH=C=CH—(CH=CH)_2—CH_2COOH$$

(*C*)

$$HC\equiv C—C\equiv C—CH=C=CH—CHOH—(CH_2)_2COOH$$

(*D*)

2–13   Tactic head-to-tail *trans*-polymerization (in the manner indicated in Figure 2–35) of olefins X—CH = CH—Y may lead to *erythro-diisotactic* (*A*) and *disyndiotactic* (*B*) polymers if the starting olefin is *trans*, and to *threo-diisotactic* (*C*) and disyndiotactic polymers if the starting olefin is *cis*. Given only this information, write Fischer projections of the three polymers. What poly-α-olefins would result from a tactic head-to-tail *cis*-polymerization (in the manner indicated in Figure 2–36)?

2–14   By the example of the spiranes below, show that the presence of four different groups on carbon is not a necessary condition for the existence of an "asymmetric carbon" as defined on p. 25.

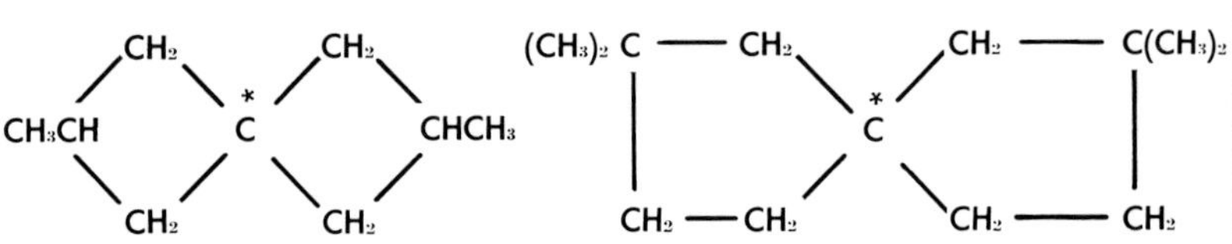

2–15   Identify diastereomeric methyl groups, if any, in the following compounds.

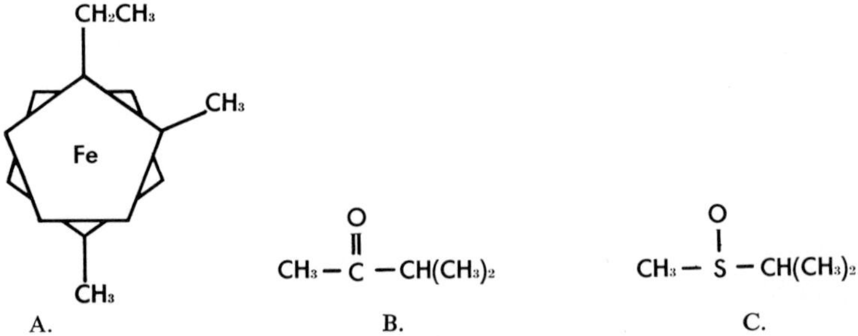

$$CH_3—\overset{\overset{\displaystyle O}{\|}}{C}—CH(CH_3)_2$$

B.

$$CH_3—\overset{\overset{\displaystyle O}{|}}{S}—CH(CH_3)_2$$

C.

A.

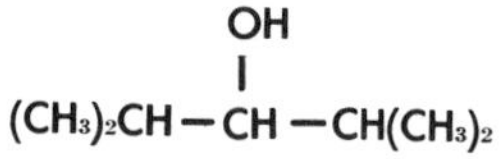

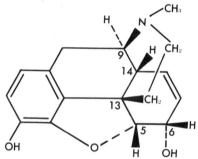

HOCH₂ CH₂OH → $HOCH_2$ CH_2OH

$$(CH_3)_2CH-\underset{\underset{\text{OH}}{|}}{CH}-CH(CH_3)_2$$

D.

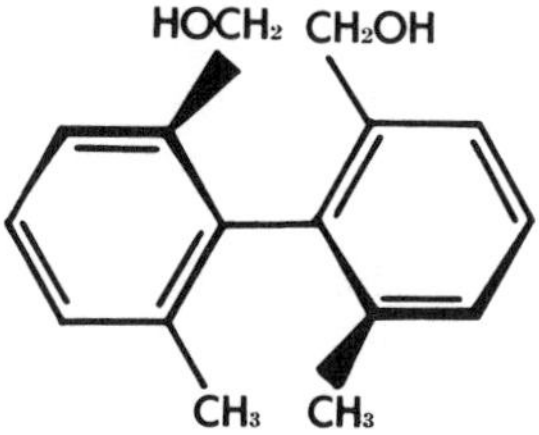

E.

2–16   Given the absolute configuration of (−)-morphine (the naturally occurring isomer) shown below, designate the configurations of the numbered asymmetric carbon atoms.

2–17   The objects described in Exercise 1–15 (b)-(d) have their analogs in cyclobutanes substituted in the 1-,2-,3-, and 4-positions by constitutionally identical, dissymmetric substituents (e.g., —CH(CH₃)-C₂H₅). List the possible stereoisomers for these analogs.

2–18   *Cis-* and *trans-*thianthrene 5,10-dioxides exist in folded conformations which are quite flexible, e.g.,

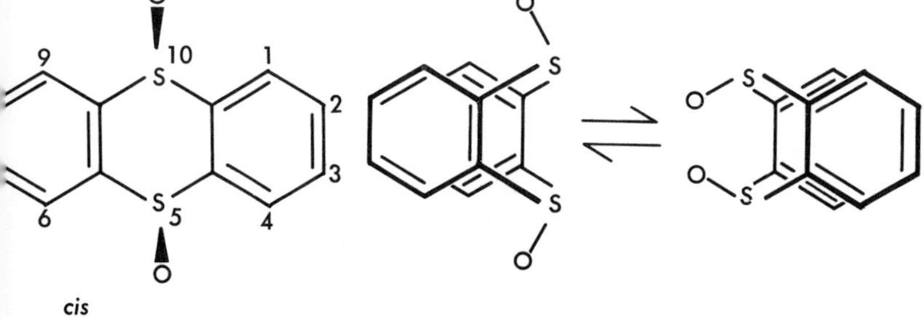

cis

Describe the stereoisomeric possibilities (configurations and conformations) for unsubstituted, monosubstituted, and disubstituted *cis-* and *trans*-thianthrene dioxides. Assume that the substituents are

the same.   Analyze the conformational relationships and compare
with those in the disubstituted chair cyclohexanes (Figure 2–30).

2–19   Various solutions of a certain substance in benzene were
examined in a 2 dm. polarimeter tube at 25°.   It was found that the
observed optical rotation of a 2% solution was +20.00°, that of a 4%
solution was +40.00°, but of that of a 5% solution was −40.00° instead
of the expected +50.00°.   How could this result be explained?

2–20   (a) Which stereoisomer of A has $\mathbf{D}_3$ symmetry? (b) What
symmetries are possible for the stereoisomers of tetrachlorocubane (all
constitutional isomers)?   Refer to Exercise 2–1P, p. 113.

A

2–21   Identify the isomer of hexamethyltricyclo[3.1.0.0$^{2.4}$]hexane
which is formed by dimerization of 1,3,3-trimethylcyclopropene and
which has $\mathbf{S}_2$ ($\equiv\mathbf{C}_i$) symmetry.

3

■ SEPARATION AND CONFIGURATION OF STEREOISOMERS

3–1   Separation of Enantiomers and Diastereomers

IN PREVIOUS sections we described in detail the structure and stereoisomerism of organic molecules. We have left thus far unanswered the questions of how stereoisomers are individually prepared and how their configurations are assigned. The problems of separation and identification are often closely related and will be dealt with in the remaining sections.

The general principle which underlies all approaches to the separation of stereoisomers has already been stated in Section 2–1. Enantiomers can only be separated by recourse to diastereomerically related intermediates, solvates, transition states, or—in the broadest sense of the word—interactions. We saw in Section 2–1 that the manual separation of enantiomorphous crystals involves a diastereomeric relationship which is introduced in the comparison of two dissymmetric crystals. In Section 2–2 we noted that optical activity involves diastereomeric interactions, in the sense that a dissymmetric medium interacts with the enantiomeric, circularly polarized components of plane-polarized light. Thus, it becomes clear that a diastereomeric relationship or interaction is the sole basis for *distinguishing* between enantiomers, and therefore for *separating* them.

Diastereomers, and diastereomerically related intermediates, differ in bonding and nonbonding intramolecular interactions. Hence, they differ in free energy relative to some common state, say the state consisting of the dissociated atoms, and they have different heats of formation. This difference, which is reflected in the gross differences in physical properties discussed in Section 2–3, is put to use in the separation of diastereomers and enantiomers. Through the manifestation of physical properties, this difference also often serves an additional function in the establishment of the configuration of a particular stereoisomer.

3–2 Optical Activation

Reactions which are carried out under nondissymmetric conditions give nondissymmetric products. If the molecules of the product are dissymmetric, the product will be racemic.

Optical activation refers to the process of securing an excess of one enantiomer over another; ideally, one enantiomer is obtained essentially free of the other. When the starting material is racemic, this process is called *resolution*. As has been implied in the preceding section, resolutions depend on the intervention of diastereomeric relationships or interactions. In this section we shall be concerned with such interactions in the ground state, whereas the next section deals with diastereoisomerism in the transition state.

The most common method of resolving a *dl*-pair *A*, e.g., a racemic acid (R)–A + (S)–A, requires combination with a dissymmetric reagent B, e.g., the base (R)–B. ((S)–B would do as well). B is the *resolving agent*. Diastereomers are formed and separated usually by fractional crystallization though occasionally by other methods such as fractional distillation or chromatography. The separated diastereomers, e.g., the salts in our example, are then decomposed and the separation of the enantiomers has thus been effected. Schematically (Eq. 3–1):

$$(R)\text{–A} + (S)\text{–A} + 2\,(R)\text{–B} \longrightarrow \begin{array}{l} (R)\text{–A·}(R)\text{–B} \rightarrow (R)\text{–A} \\ (S)\text{–A·}(R)\text{–B} \rightarrow (S)\text{–A} \end{array} \quad (3\text{–}1)$$

This method was discovered by Pasteur in 1853, who found that *dl*-tartaric acid could be thus resolved using optically active naturally occurring bases (alkaloids). Racemic bases, (*R*)–B + (*S*)–B, may be similarly resolved with acid resolving agents, e.g., (*R*)–A.

The nature of the resolving agent depends on the functionality of the compound which is to be resolved. Salts are the preferred diastereomers since they are easily and rapidly formed and decomposed, and where salts cannot be directly formed it is common practice to convert the compound into a derivative which provides a "handle" for resolution by salt formation. For example, alcohols such as 2-butanol may be resolved by fractional crystallization of the diastereomeric brucine salts of the acid phthalate derivative; after resolution, saponification of the enantiomeric acid phthalates regenerates the individual enantiomers of the alcohol. Where conversion to a suitable salt-forming derivative is not convenient, other diastereomeric derivatives (e.g., esters, hydrazones, molecular complexes) may be resorted to.

The method just described is the most important one of its kind and is rivaled in general usefulness only by the methods described in section 3–3. However, it should be stressed that numerous other methods exist which are less effective but are nonetheless of theoretical interest. Thus, racemic Tröger's base (Figure 2–23) is resolved by chromatography on a column of lactose (a dissymmetric disaccharide), and racemic hexahelicene (Figure 2–10) by the preferential crystallization of one enantiomer from a solution of the compound containing a dissymmetric complexing agent; in the last case the enantiomer forming the less stable complex in solution is the one which enriches the crystallizate.

The rare cases of *total asymmetric transformation* are of special interest. In these cases one enantiomer happens to crystallize first and thus inoculates the solution; at the same time the enantiomers interconvert in solution and the rate of interconversion is rapid compared to the rate of crystallization. Accordingly, as the crystal of one enantiomer grows, the equilibrium in solution is rapidly reestablished, and, in principle, the initially racemic substance in solution may be totally transformed into one solid enantiomer. When this solid is redissolved it converts back into the racemic material, and this process may be repeated indefinitely. An example of this sort of behavior is furnished by the benzene solvate of tri-*o*-thymotide (Figure 1–15), which forms enantiomerically homogeneous crystals from a solution of the *dl*-form in benzene where the enantiomers interconvert very rapidly. Similar behavior is shown by quartz and sodium chlorate, whose dissymmetric and optically active crystals grow from melts or solutions which are nondissymmetric. In a related case (commonly referred to as *second order asymmetric transformation*) the equilibrium between two labile diastereomers in solution is disturbed by the crystallization of one of them. A diastereomerically homogeneous material may thus be obtained by asymmetric transformation from a diastereomeric mixture. The crystallization of α- or β- glucose provides an example.

3–3 Asymmetric Synthesis and Kinetic Resolution

What has been said of diastereomerically related compounds in the ground state is applicable to diastereomerically related transition states which differ in free energy and therefore in stability. This particular difference shows up in the rates of reaction of stereoisomers, and in their rates of formation. In a crude analogy one might think of the fit of a hand (substrate) into a glove (reagent) or the clasp of a hand in another: The "feel" or excellence of the fit is reflected in the energy of the analogous transition state:

Interaction	Substrate	+	Reagent	→	Transition State
	(*hand*)		(*glove or hand*)		(*fit*)

$$
\text{diaster-eomeric}
\begin{cases}
\text{enant-iomeric}
\begin{cases}
\text{right} + \text{right} & \rightarrow \text{Favorable} \\
\text{left} + \text{left} & \rightarrow \text{Favorable}
\end{cases} & \text{low energy} \\
\text{enant-iomeric}
\begin{cases}
\text{right} + \text{left} & \rightarrow \text{Unfavorable} \\
\text{left} + \text{right} & \rightarrow \text{Unfavorable}
\end{cases} & \text{high energy}
\end{cases}
$$

The subject can best be covered systematically by considering the various possibilities which are likely to be encountered when stereoisomers react or are produced.

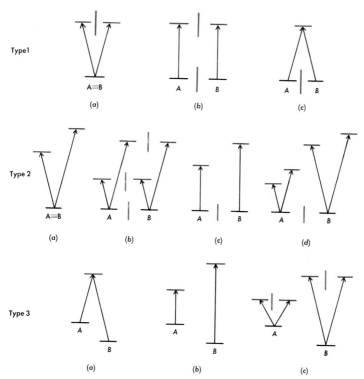

FIGURE 3–1

Types of energy relationships in the reaction and production of stereoiso-mers. Ground states are indicated by black lines, transition states by gray lines, and mirror-image relationships by vertical colored lines.

We recognize three basic types of reaction which are under kinetic control. These reaction types, energy diagrams for which are given in Figure 3–1, differ from each other as follows: In type 1, $\Delta G° = 0$ and $\Delta\Delta G^{\ddagger} = 0$, in type 2, $\Delta G° = 0$ and $\Delta\Delta G^{\ddagger} \neq 0$, and in type 3, $\Delta G° \neq 0$ and $\Delta\Delta G^{\ddagger} \neq 0$, where $G°$ and $G^{\ddagger}$ represent the free energies of ground and transition states, respectively. In order to facilitate the discussion of these various reaction types, we shall illustrate all of them by a single transformation: the alcoholysis of anhydrides. As the discussion proceeds, the reader is asked to compare the diagrams in Figure 3–1 with the appropriate reactions shown in Figures 3–2, 3–3, and 3–4.

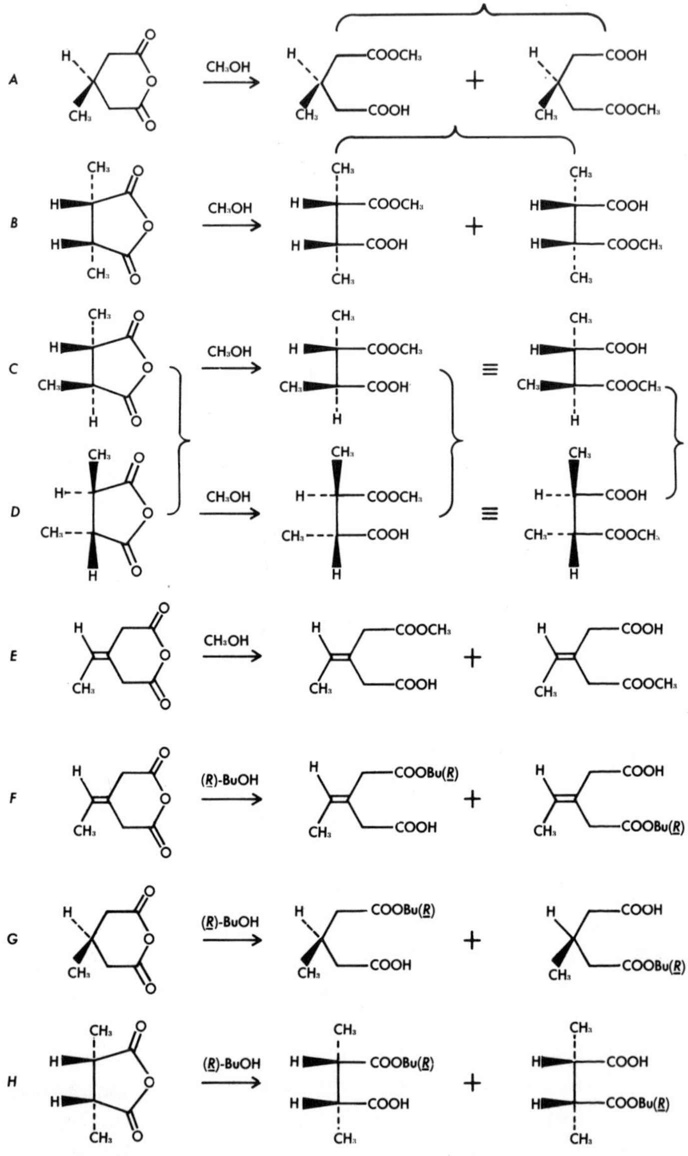

FIGURE 3–2

Illustration of reaction types (Figure 3–1) by the alcoholysis of anhydrides. Types 1a (A and B), 1b (C and D), and 2a (E–H). Brackets indicate enantiomeric relationships; Bu = 2-butyl.

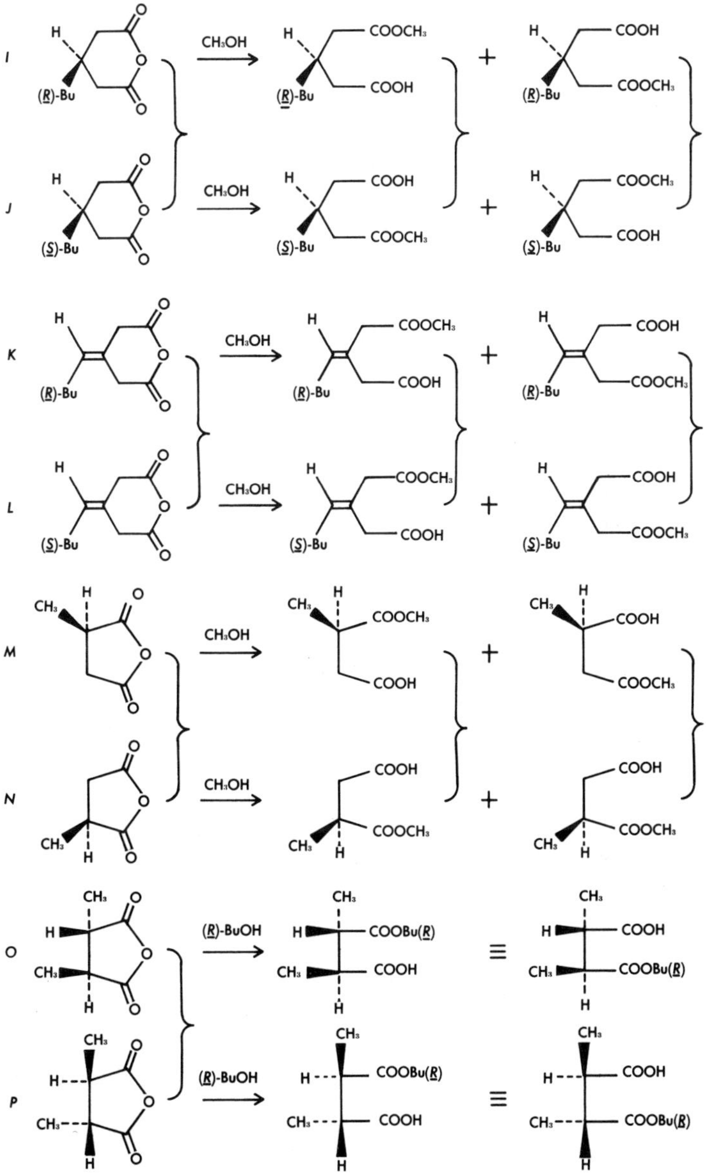

FIGURE 3–3

Illustration of reaction types (Figure 3–1) by the alcoholysis of anhydrides. Types 2b (I-N) and 2c (O and P). Brackets indicate enantiomeric relationships; Bu = 2-butyl.

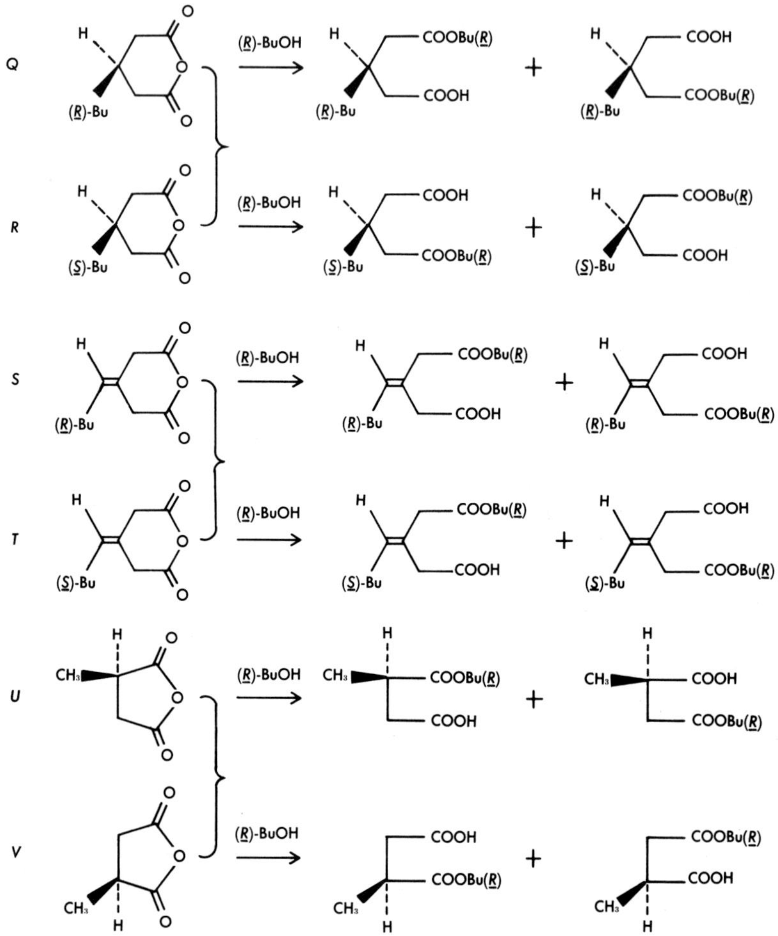

FIGURE 3–4

Illustration of reaction types (Figure 3–1) by the alcoholysis of anhydrides. Types 2d (Q–V). Brackets indicate enantiomeric relationships Bu = 2-butyl.

In reactions of type 1, the precursor is either a single nondissymmetric substance ($A{=}B$), or else A and B have the same ground state energy because they are enantiomers. In either case, $\Delta G° = 0$. The transition states also have the same energy because they are either identical or they are enantiomeric. Since $\Delta\Delta G^{\ddagger} = 0$, it follows that the two reactions occur at exactly the same rate, and the products of reaction must be found in exactly equal amounts.

Reaction type 1a ($A \equiv B$) may be exemplified by the methanolysis of β-methylglutaric anhydride to *dl*-methyl hydrogen β-methyl-glutarate (Figure 3–2*A*). The β-carbon of the anhydride has two substituents which are enantiomerically related. A carbon atom of formula type $Cxyz_2$ is sometimes called a *meso carbon atom*. The relationship of the substituents z on a *meso* carbon atom is precisely the one discussed for enantiomeric protons in $CxyH_2$ (section 2–4). For purposes of comparison, the methanolysis of a true *meso* compound is shown to give analogous results (Figure 3–2*B*).

When one of the groups z on a *meso* carbon atom $Cxyz_2$ reacts even under nondissymmetric conditions, it becomes different (z') from the other and the *meso* carbon atom becomes an asymmetric carbon atom. It follows that if the reagent or catalyst is dissymmetric, diastereomeric products or transition states must result, as will be discussed in connection with reaction types 2.

Another example of type 1a is the lithium aluminum hydride reduction of 2-butanone to *dl*-2-butanol. Formalistically, the double bond in 2-butanone represents the two enantiomerically related substituents in $Cxyz_2$, and the carbonyl carbon in ketones of the type $xyCO$ and in all aldehydes except formaldehyde may therefore also be regarded as a *meso* carbon atom.

We include among reactions of type 1a those which lead to a single product *via* enantiomeric transition states, as in the decarboxylation of methylmalonic acid to propionic acid. This reaction has its formal analog in the decarboxylation of methylethylmalonic acid to *dl*-2-methylbutanoic acid. The substituted malonic acids have *meso* carbon atoms.

Reaction type 1b (*A* and *B* are enantiomers) is illustrated by the methanolysis of *dl*-dimethylsuccinic anhydride (*C* and *D*, Figure 3–2). Each enantiomer of starting anhydride gives a corresponding enantiomer of product, and racemic anhydride affords racemic acid ester. Note that in this example the two carbonyl groups in each enantiomer are identical since the molecule has C_2 symmetry, with the C_2 axis bisecting the anhydride group. A second example is the S_N2 reaction of (*R*)- and (*S*)- 2-butyl-*p*-toluenesulfonate with sodium acetate to give optically active (*S*)- or (*R*)-2-butyl acetate, respectively. We include among reactions of type 1b those in which the starting enantiomers *A* and *B* give the identical product via enantiomeric transition states, e.g., the oxidation of (*R*)- or (*S*)-2-butanol to 2-butanone. Type 1c in Figure 3–1 is illustrated by the reaction of (R)- or (S)-2-bromoöctane with sodium bromide, which gives (*via* a reversible S_N2 reaction) racemic 2-bromoöctane. In the last example the transition state has a σ plane perpendicular to the Br—C—Br axis and is the same whichever (A or B) is the starting material.

In the preceding examples, the problem of diastereoisomerism does not arise. Where it does, it is inevitable that among the several diastereomers which can be formed or destroyed in a reaction, one is formed or destroyed at a different rate than the other. This behavior is called *stereoselectivity*. In reaction types 2 and 3, $\Delta\Delta G^{\ddagger} \neq 0$ whether $\Delta G^{\circ} = 0$ (type 2) or $\Delta G^{\circ} \neq 0$ (type 3). It follows that all of the reactions of types 2 and 3 in which two or more stereoisomers are produced are *stereoselective,* even if the deviation of the ratio of products from unity is too small to be detected by ordinary means. The degree of stereoselectivity depends on the magnitude of $\Delta\Delta G^{\ddagger}$: the greater $\Delta\Delta G^{\ddagger}$, the greater the stereoselectivity. It is customary to indicate the degree of stereoselectivity qualitatively, e.g., "highly stereoselective," "extremely low stereoselectivity," etc., or quantitatively, by the *per cent stereoselectivity* which is given by $100(a - b)/(a + b)$, where a and b are the amounts of diastereomers formed.

Since $\Delta G^{\circ} = 0$, reactions of type 2 resemble those of type 1. In reaction type 2a, the precursor is a single nondissymmetric substance ($A \equiv B$). In reaction types 2b-d, A and B have the same ground state because they are enantiomers.

Reaction type 2a is analogous to type 1a. An example of this type is the highly stereoselective catalytic semihydrogenation of 2-butyne, which gives a mixture of *cis*- and *trans*-2-butenes, with the former in great excess over the latter. A closely related example is the methanolysis of the anhydride shown in Figure 3–2E, in which the two carbonyl groups are diastereomerically related. Methanolysis results in two nondissymmetric diastereomers. In the alcoholyses *F–H* (Figure 3–2), the starting anhydride is also nondissymmetric, but the reacting alcohol is now dissymmetric and the product is a mixture of two dissymmetric diastereomers which are produced in unequal amounts. This result is independent of whether the carbonyl groups in the anhydride are diastereomerically related (Figure 3–2F), or whether they are enantiomerically related (G and $H,$ Figure 3–2). A reaction in which new dissymmetric groupings (e.g., asymmetric carbons) are produced in unequal amounts is termed *asymmetric synthesis.* Alcoholyses *F–H* in Figure 3–2 follow this definition. Alcoholysis *E* in Figure 3–2 shows that reactions of type 2a do not necessarily result in asymmetric syntheses. We also include among reactions of type 2a those which lead to a single product *via* diastereomeric transition states, as in the decarboxylation of methylmalonic acid in the presence of brucine or some other dissymmetric catalyst. The product is propionic acid, which is incapable of stereoisomerism. This reaction has its formal analog in the asymmetric synthesis of 2-methylbutanoic acid by decarboxylation of methylethylmalonic acid in the presence of a dissymmetric catalyst. The product in this case is optically active.

Asymmetric syntheses are particularly effective in biological systems. The reactions take place on enzyme surfaces, and generally the stereoselectivity is for all intents and purposes 100%. By contrast, most nonbiological processes fall well below this mark. Some of the more instructive enzymatic reactions of type 2a are those in which the substrates are compounds with *meso*-carbon atoms. Thus, the asymmetric phosphorylation of glycerol by adenosine triphosphate (ATP) in the presence of the enzyme glycerokinase gives (*R*)-α-glycerophosphate as the sole product. Similarly, the asymmetric reduction of acetaldehyde-1-*d* with reduced nicotinamide adenine diphosphate (NAD), i.e., NAD*H,* in the presence of the enzyme yeast alcohol dehydrogenase yields only (*S*)-ethanol-1-*d,* whereas the asymmetric reduction of acetaldehyde with the deuterated analog, NAD*D,* yields only (*R*)-ethanol-1-*d.* The high stereoselectivity of the reaction is explained by the schematic model shown in Figure 3–5. The molecule is held tightly against the enzyme surface. Since the enzyme is dissymmetric and since the attack of dissymmetric reagents on enantiomeric sites at *meso* atoms gives rise to diastereomeric transition states (Figure 3–2*G*), it follows that the two faces of the carbonyl group (which might be thought of as *enantiomeric faces*) do not interact equally with the enzyme surface. If the difference between the favorable and unfavorable arrangements (Figure 3–5) is great enough, the high stereoselectivity of the asymmetric reduction is accounted for. The function of the enzyme is clearly that of an asymmetric catalyst. Similar asymmetric reduction of ketones or aldehydes not involving enzymes (as by the use of optically active diisopinocampheylborane, isobornyloxymagnesium halides, or 2-

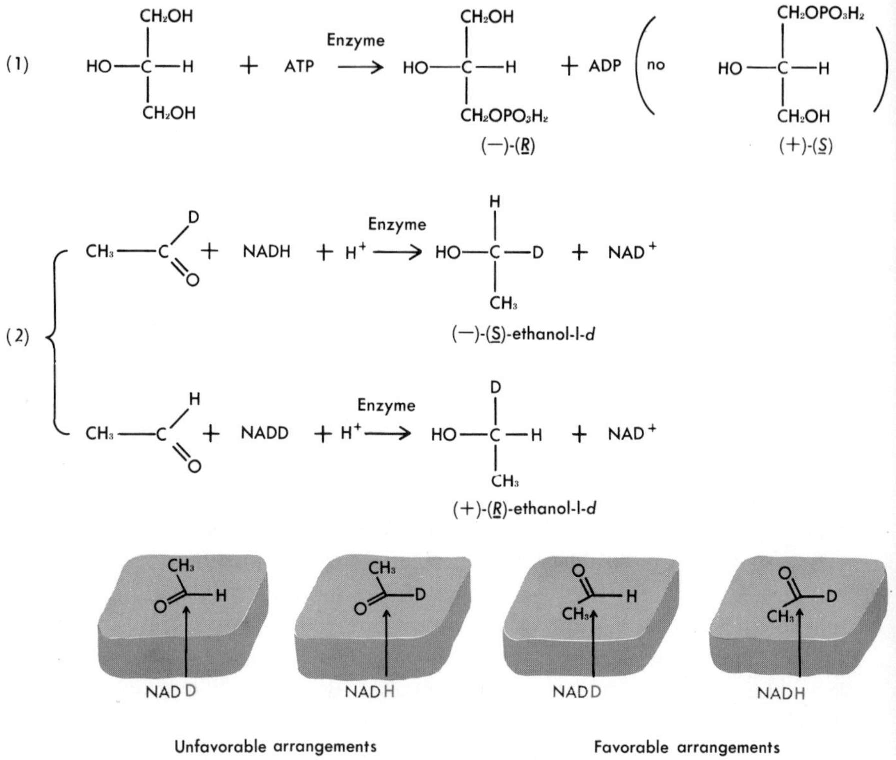

(1)

$$CH_2OH \quad HO—C—H \quad + \quad ATP \quad \xrightarrow{\text{Enzyme}} \quad CH_2OH \quad HO—C—H \quad + \quad ADP \quad \left(no \quad CH_2OPO_3H_2 \quad HO—C—H \right)$$

$$CH_2OH \qquad\qquad CH_2OPO_2H_2 \qquad\qquad\qquad CH_2OH$$

$$(-)\text{-}(\underline{R}) \qquad\qquad (+)\text{-}(\underline{S})$$

(2)

$$CH_3—C\overset{D}{\underset{O}{\diagup}} \quad + \quad NADH \quad + \quad H^+ \xrightarrow{\text{Enzyme}} \quad HO—\overset{H}{\underset{CH_3}{C}}—D \quad + \quad NAD^+$$

$$(-)\text{-}(\underline{S})\text{-ethanol-1-}d$$

$$CH_3—C\overset{H}{\underset{O}{\diagup}} \quad + \quad NADD \quad + \quad H^+ \xrightarrow{\text{Enzyme}} \quad HO—\overset{D}{\underset{CH_3}{C}}—H \quad + \quad NAD^+$$

$$(+)\text{-}(\underline{R})\text{-ethanol-1-}d$$

Unfavorable arrangements	Favorable arrangements
NAD D NAD H	NAD D NAD H

FIGURE 3–5

*Some enzymatic reactions of type 2*a.

methylbutylmagnesium chloride) are generally a good deal less stereoselective.

In reactions of type 2b the starting material is dissymmetric and two enantiomers (*A* and *B*) exist, each capable of leading to two diastereomeric transition states. Hence, there are two sets of two transition states to consider, related as shown in Figure 3–1. An example is the dehydration of (*R*)- and (*S*)-2-butanol to give *cis*- and *trans*-2-butenes. Each enantiomer gives the identical mixture of geometric isomers. The dehydration of 2-butanol to 1-butene represents a separate reaction of type 1b, superimposed on 2b.

Methanolysis of the racemic anhydrides shown in *I–L* of Figure 3–3 leads to a mixture of diastereomeric *dl*-pairs, which must be produced in unequal amounts. Another example of an asymmetric synthesis of type 2b is the radical fluorination of *dl*-2-chlorobutane, which under certain conditions gives a mixture of 67% *dl*-erythro- and 33% *dl*-threo-2-chloro-3-fluorobutane; its variant, the radical chlorination of *dl*-2-chlorobutane, gives a mixture of 71% *meso*- and 29% *dl*-2,3-dichlorobutane. In 2-chlorobutane the methylene hydrogens are diastereomeric in the ground state (Section 2–4), and the halogenation converts the molecule into conventional diastereomers.

A point worth noting in the preceding discussion is that in some of the asymmetric syntheses a new asymmetric carbon is created in the presence of the old without destruction of the latter, whereas in others the inducing "center" is destroyed in the course of the asymmetric synthesis. Asymmetric syntheses of the first kind, which might be called *conservative,* are illustrated by the halogenations of 2-chlorobutane. Asymmetric syntheses of the second kind, which might be called *self-immolative,* are illustrated by asymmetric hydride transfer reactions; for example, in the reduction of methyl *t*-butyl ketone by optically pure 2-methylbutylmagnesium chloride, the reduction product, methyl *t*-butyl carbinol, has been produced in optically active form at the expense of the dissymmetry of the Grignard reagent, which has been lost in the conversion to 2-methyl-1-butene.

Since the starting compounds in reaction type 2b are by definition dissymmetric, *meso*-compounds or compounds containing *meso* carbon atoms cannot undergo this type of asymmetric synthesis.

We shall conclude our discussion of reaction type 2b with three more illustrations. The first is the lithium aluminum hydride reduction of *dl*-3-phenyl-2-butanone, which gives a mixture of *threo*- and *erythro*-3-phenyl-2-butanols, the former diastereomer predominating over the latter. Addition to the two sides of the carbonyl groups in this example is stereochemically equivalent to the substitution of the diastereomeric methylene hydrogens by halogen in the preceding examples and to the methanolysis of the two diastereomerically related carbonyl groups in anhydrides *I–L* (Figure 3–3). In short, we may think of the two faces of the carbonyl group as *diastereomeric faces.*

The second example is the decarboxylation of *dl*-sec-butylmalonic acid. Each enantiomer of this compound gives rise to two diastereomeric transition states but to only a single product, 3-

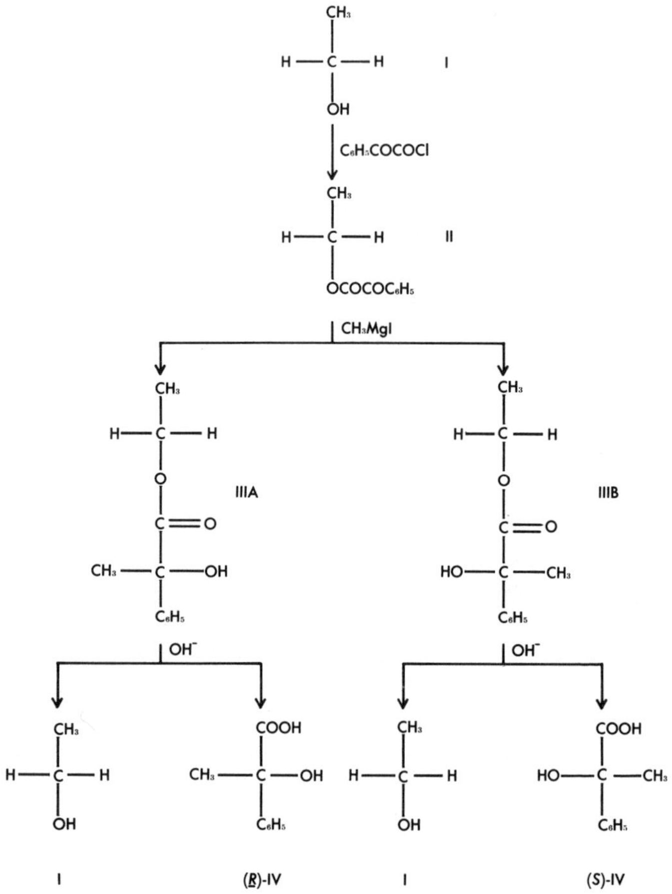

FIGURE 3–6

The atrolactic acid synthesis as an illustration of reaction type 2b. Left,

methylpentanoic acid.   This compound has no diastereomers. The product of the decarboxylation is therefore *dl*-3-methylpentanoic acid, and this result shows that reactions of type 2b do not necessarily lead to asymmetric syntheses.

Our final illustration, an asymmetric synthesis of type 2b, is the atrolactic acid synthesis (Figure 3–6).   When ethanol (I) is esterified with phenylglyoxalyl chloride and the resulting ethyl phenylglyoxylate (II) is treated with methylmagnesium iodide, the methyl groups may add either to one or the other of the two *nondissymmetric; right, asymmetric (Fischer projections).*

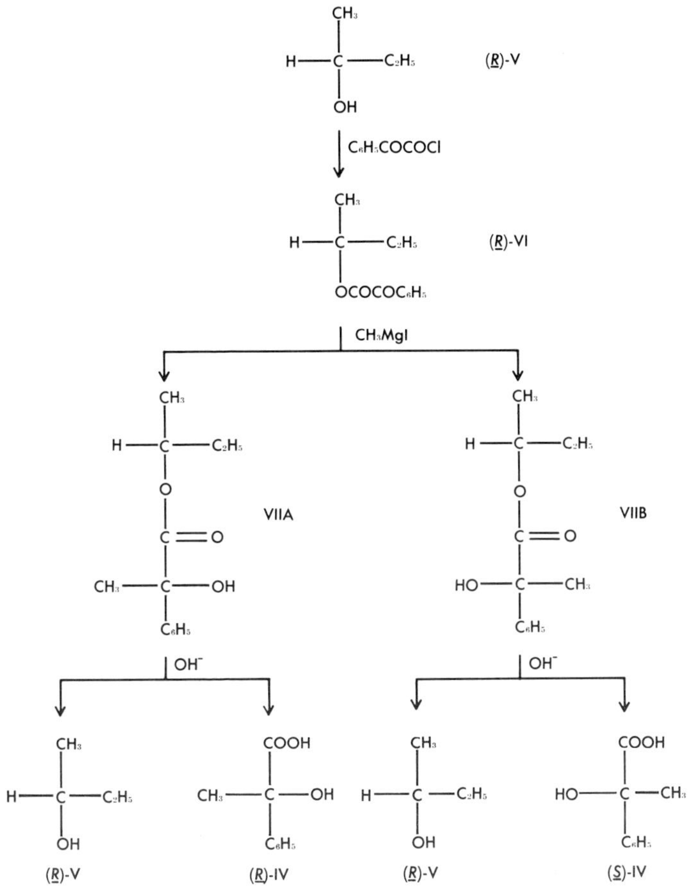

enantiomeric faces of the ketonic carbonyl group. This approach is reaction type 1a, and the two transition states bear an enantiomeric relationship to each other, as in the lithium aluminum hydride reduction of 2-butanone. The products of the reaction, III*A* and III*B,* are enantiomers and the two isomers are produced at the same rate and therefore in the same quantities. Saponification will therefore result in ethanol plux an *equimolar* mixture of (*R*)- and (*S*)-atrolactic acid (IV), i.e., *racemic* IV. On the other hand, if the starting alcohol is (*R*)-2-butanol (V) and the corresponding phenylglyoxylate (VI) is treated with methylmagnesium iodide, addition of methyl group to the two diastereomeric faces of the ketonic carbonyl group will result in VII*A* and VII*B,* which are diastereomers, and which will be produced at unequal rates and therefore in unequal quantities (reaction type 2b). Complete saponification of the ester mixture will therefore result in the recovery of the original (*R*)-2-butanol plus an *unequal* mixture of (*R*)- and (*S*)-atrolactic acid.   In this particular example, (−)-(*R*)-atrolactic acid is the predominant enantiomer and the asymmetric synthesis has resulted in optical activation.   It is seen that (*R*)-2-butanol simply induces optical activity without itself being destroyed; in principle the inducing alcohol could be recycled indefinitely to produce any desired quantity of optically active albeit optically impure atrolactic acid.   Accordingly, (*R*)-2-butanol functions as an asymmetric catalyst by governing the relative rates of formation of the diastereomeric esters VII*A* and VII*B*. If (*S*)-2-butanol had been used in the preceding scheme, the ratio of VII*A* and VII*B* would simply have been reversed, and the product after saponification would have been (+)-(*S*)-atrolactic acid of the same optical purity as the enantiomer in the preceding scheme.

Reactions of type 2b are restricted to those in which the enantiomers *A* and *B* react with nondissymmetric reagents such as chlorine, lithium aluminum hydride, or methylmagnesium iodide. In reactions of this type each isomer gives rise to two diastereomeric transition states, and the populations of these two transition states is exactly the same starting from either *A* or *B*.   For the sake of completeness, we also include in type 2b those reactions in which the two transition states originating from each enantiomer are constitutionally isomeric.   For example, in the methanolysis of the enantiomeric anhydrides *M* and *N* (Figure 3–3), starting with *dl*-anhydride, the two *dl*-pairs which are produced in unequal quantities are constitutional isomers.

In contrast to reactions of type 2b, reactions of types 2c and 2d are those in which a dissymmetric substance (*A* and *B* are enantiomers) reacts with a dissymmetric reagent or catalyst.   Under these conditions *A* and *B* *must* react at different rates.

An example of reaction type 2c is the alcoholysis of *dl-trans*-dimethylsuccinic anhydride with (*R*)-butanol (*O* and *P*, Figure 3–3).   The product of the alcoholysis is a single pair of diastereomers. The simplicity of this result is due to the identity of the two carbonyl groups in each enantiomer of the anhydride (C_2 symmetry). The two diastereomers are produced in unequal amounts because their rates of formation are different. Therefore, the two enantiomers are consumed at different rates. Quantitatively, this problem may be treated as follows.

Consider the simple case of a first-order reaction, where the rate of disappearance of a substance X is proportional to the amount of X left in solution. This can be expressed analytically by saying that the relative concentration of X, i.e. $[X]$, at any time equals $exp(-kt)$, where k is the specific rate constant of the reaction. In the reaction of a racemic mixture (A and B) with a nondissymmetric reagent, $k_A = k_B$. Therefore, $exp(-k_At) = exp(-k_Bt)$, and $[X_A]$ is equal to $[X_B]$ over the complete time interval $0 < t < \infty$. This is, of course, reaction type 1b, exemplified by the saponification of the racemic ester mixture IIIA–IIIB (Figure 3–6) and by the methanolysis of the racemic anhydride mixture $C-D$ (Figure 3–2). However, in the reaction of a racemic mixture A and B with a dissymmetric reagent, $k_A \neq k_B$. Now $exp(-k_At) \neq exp(-k_Bt)$, and $[X_A]$ can never be equal to $[X_B]$ except at the very start ($t = 0$). This is shown graphically in Figure 3–7, where it has been assumed, for the sake of simplicity, that $k_A = 2$ and $k_B = 1$ (i.e., A is more reactive than B) so that at any given time t, $[X_A]/[X_B] = exp(-t)$. This indicates that at the beginning of the reaction, when $t = 0$, our mixture is racemic and $[X_A] = [X_B]$, but, as the reaction proceeds, $[X_A]/[X_B]$ decreases from unity at $t = 0$ and approaches zero at $t = \infty$. In other words, there is a permanent and steadily increasing excess of B, the less reactive enantiomer, over A, the more reactive enantiomer, expressed by the ratio $[X_A]/[X_B]$. This excess, when given by $[X_B]-[X_A]$, follows the curve in Figure 3–7. At the inversion time, t_{max}, which is indicated by the colored arrow in Figure 3–7, $[X_B]-[X_A]$ achieves its maximum value. The physical significance of t_{max} is the following: Since $k_A = 2k_B$, the *specific* rate of reaction of A is always twice the *specific* rate of reaction of B. However, the actual rate of reaction is the product in each case of the specific rate constant and the concentration. Up to the time of t_{max} the enantiomer with the greater specific rate, A, has reacted more rapidly. The amount of A has therefore been depleted relative to the amount of B until, at t_{max}, the product $k_A[X_A]$ has become equal to the product $k_B[X_B]$.

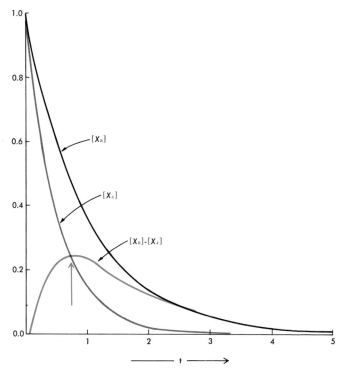

FIGURE 3–7

Plot of (a) exp(−t) vs. *t* (*black line*), (b) exp(−2t) vs. *t* (*gray line*), (c) (exp(−t) −exp(−2t)) vs. *t* (*colored line*). *The colored arrow indicates* t_{max}.

From there on, *B* becomes the more rapidly reacting enantiomer.

The preceding example shows that interruption at any time during the course of the reaction gives the starting substance enriched in one of the enantiomers; the enrichment increases with *t* and is expressed by the optical purity $([X_B] - [X_A]) / ([X_B] + [X_A])$. This type of optical activation is termed a *kinetic resolution* because it is in a sense a separation of enantiomers based on differential rates of reaction. Alternatively one may speak of an *asymmetric destruction,* since one of the enantiomers is destroyed, i.e., removed by reaction, more rapidly than the other. Pasteur discovered the first example of a kinetic resolution when he found, in 1858, that the fermentation of racemic ammonium tartrate with the mold *Penicillium glaucum* preferentially consumed the (+)-form and left the $(-)$-form untouched. This tremendous stereoselectivity is characteristic of enzyme reactions, as we saw earlier. One other example may be mentioned: Heart muscle dehydrogenase oxidizes only (S)-but not (R)-malic acid. These two examples illustrate the term *stereospecificity,* which is used here to signify that stereoisomerically different starting materials (e.g., the enantiomeric malic acids) give rise to different products or just differ in reactivity. Stereospecificity may be qualitatively or quantitatively estimated in the same manner as stereoselectivity. Virtually all enzymatic kinetic resolutions are highly stereospecific processes. Enzymatic stereospecificity is qualitatively demonstrated in the dramatic differences which are exhibited by biologically active enantiomers in their interaction with the human organism. Thus, $(+)$-morphine is a powerful analgesic whereas the mirror-image form, $(-)$-morphine, is inactive. Similarly, one of the enantiomers of chloramphenicol is an effective antibiotic whereas the other is not and one of the enantiomers of asparagine has a sweet taste whereas the other does not.

Enzymatic stereospecificity does not necessarily lead to kinetic resolution of *dl*-pairs, provided that certain structural conditions are satisfied. This is strikingly illustrated in the aconitase-catalyzed degradation of citric acid (I, Figure 3–8). When a racemic mixture of dideuteriocitrate (II, Figure 3–8) is enzymatically degraded, the two enantiomers react at essentially identical rates. Yet the reaction is completely stereospecific, as can be deduced from the fact that the (R)-isomer gives only α-ketoglutarate whereas the (S)-isomer gives only dideuterio-α-ketoglutarate. The explanation is the following. The middle carbon of citric acid I is a *meso* carbon atom. Focusing our attention on the enantiomeric -CH_2COOH groupings which are attached to the central carbon atom, it can be readily seen (Figure 3–8) that the interactions of the two groupings with the dissymmetric aconitase are diastereomeric (reaction type 2a). As we have seen in the asymmetric reduction of acetaldehyde, enzymatic reactions of this type are highly stereoselective. Accordingly, only that enantiomeric -CH_2COOH grouping in I which has the favorable interaction will be degraded. Returning to the case of citrate II, it is seen that the two groupings -CH_2COOH and -CD_2COOH are enantiomeric in all essential respects and that the deuterium only functions as a label of the stereochemistry. In the (R)-isomer the labeled grouping has

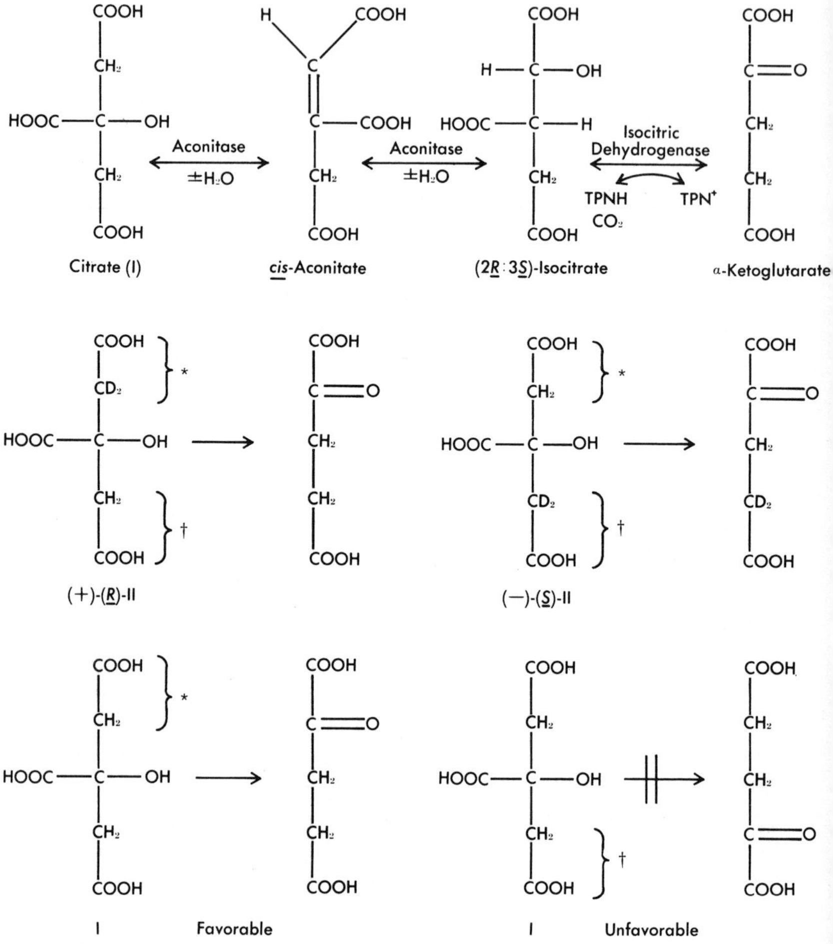

FIGURE 3–8

Asymmetric citric acid degradation. Top row, over-all reaction sequence. Middle row, degradation of enantiomeric dideuteriocitrates (II). Bottom row, degradation of citrate (I). Bracket indicates site of interaction with aconitase. Asterisk (*) signifies favorable diastereomeric interaction, whereas dagger (†) represents unfavorable diastereomeric interaction (Fischer projections).

the favorable stereochemistry and the unlabeled grouping the unfavorable stereochemistry, whereas in the (S)-isomer the labeled grouping has the unfavorable stereochemistry and the unlabeled grouping the favorable stereochemistry. The consequences have been discussed.

A final example of reaction type 2c, sometimes called an *absolute asymmetric synthesis,* is illustrated by the kinetic resolution of racemic α-azidopropionic acid dimethylamide (CH_3CHN_3–$CON(CH_3)_2$). This reaction is effected by irradiation with circularly polarized light in a region (280–310 mμ) where the compound has an absorption band. The absorbed light causes a photochemical decomposition to occur, and the rate of decomposition depends on the quantity of light absorbed. We learned in section 2–2 that a dissymmetric substance has different extinction coefficients for right and left circularly polarized light ($\epsilon_L \neq \epsilon_R$). By the same token, enantiomeric substances have different extinction coefficients for circularly polarized light of the same chirality. The enantiomers therefore absorb light to slightly different extents, and the rates of the photochemical decomposition of the two enantiomers are not the same. Recovered unreacted α-azidopropionic acid dimethylamide is therefore optically active. Dissymmetric *radiation,* rather than dissymmetric chemicals, have here been employed to effect this asymmetric destruction.

Reaction type 2d is a more complex version of the asymmetric synthesis type 2b and the kinetic resolution type 2c. In type 2b each enantiomer reacts at the same rate *via* two diastereomeric transition states. In type 2d the two enantiomers react at different rates, each *via* two diastereomeric transition states. In contrast to 2b, the four transition states all differ in energy, and the result is a kinetic resolution of *A* and *B.* This type of reaction is illustrated by the alcoholyses of anhydrides *Q–T* (Figure 3–4). In the alcoholysis of *Q* and *R*, the β-carbon atom of glutaric anhydride becomes an asymmetric carbon (as in the related examples *A, G, I,* and *J,* Figures 3–2 and 3–3) and an asymmetric synthesis has thus occurred. At the same time, since *Q* and *R* react at different rates, a kinetic resolution has also been achieved. This example serves to illustrate the generalization that asymmetric syntheses and kinetic resolutions are often different sides of the same coin, i.e., inseparable if distinct aspects of the same phenomenon. The same point may be made even more directly by considering the decarboxylation of *dl-sec*-butylmalonic acid in the presence of a dissymmetric catalyst such as brucine. In the course of the reaction, one enantiomer of the precursor decarboxylates more rapidly than the other, and, if the reaction is interrupted, the starting malonic acid will be optically active (see exercise 3–11). At the same time, the only product, 3-methylpentanoic acid, is also produced in optically active form. In this single reaction, the optical activation of the precursor is a kinetic resolution whereas the optical activation of the product is an asymmetric synthesis.

For the sake of completeness, we include in type 2d those reactions in which the two transition states originating from each enantiomer are constitutionally isomeric. For example, in the kinetic resolution of anhydrides U and V by alcoholysis (Figure 3–4) each enantiomer gives rise to two constitutional isomers, and the two sets of constitutional isomers are in turn diastereomerically related.

In reactions of type 3 the ground states of the precursors differ, and we are therefore dealing with a comparison between two diastereomers. If the diastereomers are dissymmetric, each diastereomer exists in enantiomeric forms and the reaction pattern of each individual diastereomer then falls into one of the two major categories dealt with before, i.e., types 1 and 2. Since the basic principles for these two types have already been discussed, we shall restrict the remaining discussion to a few examples illustrating some (but certainly not all) of the possibilities which may be inherent in type 3.

The simplest variant of type 3 is 3a in Figure 3–1, where the transition state is common to both diastereomers. We have encountered this example in the interconversion of the isomeric 2-butenes (Figure 2–10). A slightly more complex situation arises for the case in which the transition states are also diastereomeric (3b). An example of type 3b is provided by the decarboxylation of the acid methyl ester of *sec*-butylmalonic acid to methyl 3-methylpentanoate. The enantiomeric precursors decarboxylate according to type 1b. However, the diastereomers of the precursor decarboxylate according to type 3b to give either a single enantiomer of the product ester or to give the racemic ester, depending on whether the configurations of the two diastereomers at the asymmetric carbon bearing the methyl group are the same or opposite.

Type 3c is illustrated by the addition of bromine to *cis*- and *trans*-2-pentene to give *dl-threo-* and *dl-erythro*-2,3-dibromopentane, respectively; in each case the product is essentially diastereomerically pure. This is an example of an essentially completely stereospecific reaction and for reactions of lower stereospecificity the diagram for type 3c in Figure 3–1 must be modified by the addition of four more arrows which complete all the possible pathways available to the system.

Numerous other combinations might be contemplated involving the various stereochemical types we have thus far encountered, but the reader at this point should be in a position to analyze these more complex transformations. We conclude this section, in which we have placed so much emphasis on the stereospecificity of dissymmetric processes, especially those catalyzed by enzymes, by citing as our last example the fumarase catalyzed hydration of fumarate, a reaction which points up once more the extraordinary specificity of enzymatic processes. The hydration involves an equilibrium which may be written as (Formula I):

$$
\begin{array}{ccc}
\underset{\diagdown\diagup}{\overset{\text{H}\qquad\text{COOH}}{}} & & \overset{1}{\text{COOH}} \\
\text{C} & +\,H_2O \quad \overset{\text{fumarase}}{\rightleftharpoons} \quad & \text{HO}\!-\!\overset{2}{\text{C}}\!-\!\text{H} \\
\| & & | \\
\text{C} & & \text{H}\!-\!\overset{3}{\text{C}}\!-\!\text{H} \\
\underset{\text{HOOC}\quad\text{H}}{\diagup\diagdown} & & \overset{4}{\text{COOH}}
\end{array}
\qquad \text{I}
$$

First, the hydration is specific for the *trans*-isomer only; maleate is unreactive under the same conditions. Second, only one of the two possible enantiomers of malic acid is formed, i.e., the (2S)-isomer. Third, when D_2O is used in place of H_2O, only one of the four possible stereoisomers of 2-hydroxysuccinic acid-3-*d* is formed, namely, the (2S:3R)-isomer. Note that this is a reversible reaction, and that only the deuterium and not the protium is removed *and* replaced. If protium were to take the place of deuterium, only one of the two diastereomeric hydrogens at C-3 (which could be distinguished by NMR) would be removed and replaced, always at the stereochemically identical site!

3–4   Absolute Configuration

The configuration of diastereomers is often easily determined because gross differences in the physical properties thoroughly characterize the isomers. For example, one of the isomers of 1,2-dichloroethene has a dipole moment of zero whereas the other has a dipole moment of 1.89 D.   Similarly, one of the isomers of cyclo-propane-1,2-dicarboxylic acid is resolvable whereas the other is not.   In both examples the identity of the *cis-* and *trans*-isomers is thus clearly established.   We note incidentally that the nonresolva-bility of *cis*-cyclopropane-1,2-dicarboxylic acid may be positively demonstrated by preparing and resolving the acid ethyl ester which, on saponification or esterification (with ethanol), gives optically *inactive* diacid or diethyl ester, respectively.   The mere failure to resolve a compound represents negative evidence of the most dubi-ous kind, since the difficulty may be trivial in origin (e.g., an unsuitable choice of a resolving agent).

Although in other cases the assignment may be less unequivocal, the principle of ascribing diastereomeric identity on the basis of characteristic physical properties or chemical reactivities remains the same.   However, it is also possible to determine the configura-tion of individual diastereomers by direct structural analysis, in particular by analysis based on X-ray diffraction.   The information obtained by this method yields the structural parameters (inter-nuclear and dihedral angles, internuclear distances) which are necessary for a three-dimensional picture of the molecule.   How-ever, ordinary X-ray crystallography does not provide the informa-tion which is required to establish the chirality or absolute config-uration of one of a pair of enantiomers.   In other words, it is not possible to distinguish between enantiomers by the ordinary meth-ods of X-ray diffraction.

This difficulty can be overcome through the method of anomalous X-ray scattering.   In this method use is made of the fact that when the wave length of the incident beam is slightly shorter than the absorption edge of an atom in a molecule, the inner electrons of that atom are excited and fluorescence occurs.   In anomalous scattering, and in contrast to ordinary diffraction, the phase lag between the waves scattered from successive layers in the crystals differs according to whether the layer containing the fluor-escing atom is in front of or behind other reference atoms, all relative to the source of radiation.   Under these circumstances, enantiomeric crystal structures give different diffraction patterns which can be interpreted in terms of the spatial disposition of the nuclei in the crystal relative to the source of radiation, i.e., in terms of absolute configuration.

The conditions under which anomalous scattering occurs are

fairly critical since certain relationships between the frequency of the incident beam and the atomic number of the scattering atom must be satisfied. Several elements have been found suitable as anomalous scattering centers, notably, iodine, bromine, and rubidium.

The elucidation of the absolute configurations of (+)-tartaric acid and of (−)-isoleucine exemplifies the application of this method to key substances in configurational correlations (section 3–5). These two compounds, whose absolute configurations are shown (Formula II), were examined in the crystalline state as the sodium rubidium salt and as the hydrobromide salt, respectively.

$$
\begin{array}{ccc}
\text{COOH} & & \text{COOH} \\
| & & | \\
\text{H—C—OH} & & \text{H—C—NH}_2 \\
| & & | \\
\text{HO—C—H} & & \text{H—C—CH}_3 \\
| & & | \\
\text{COOH} & & \text{C}_2\text{H}_5 \\
\text{(+)-Tartaric acid} & & \text{(−)-Isoleucine}
\end{array}
\qquad \text{II}
$$

3–5   Configurational Correlations by Chemical Methods

Once absolute standards have been established, as described in the previous section, the absolute configuration of other dissymmetric groupings may be determined by correlation to that of the standard grouping. Relative configuration thus becomes absolute configuration. Two approaches to the realization of such correlations have been employed: in one, chemical reactions are at the basis of the correlation, whereas in the other the correlation rests on a comparison by physical methods. In this section we shall discuss the first approach and in the following section the second one.

Configurations may be unequivocally correlated by chemical reactions which do not affect the stereochemical integrity of the dissymmetric grouping; in the case of asymmetric atoms, this means that the reactions do not involve the making or breaking of bonds joined to the asymmetric atom. Extensive correlations of this sort have been carried out in the carbohydrate, terpene, steroid, and amino acid series of compounds which owe their interest to the relevance of these substances to biological processes. A simple example is the establishment of the configuration of (+)-xylose as

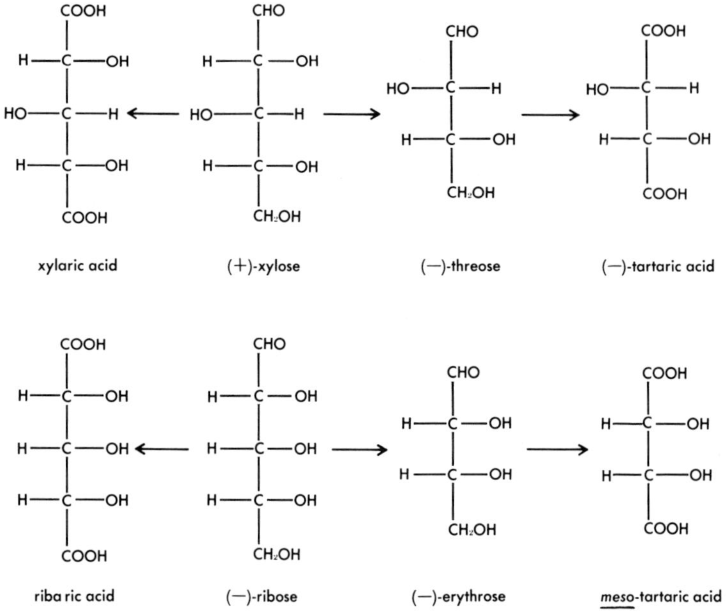

FIGURE 3–9

Configurational correlation of some carbohydrates by chemical methods (Fischer projections).

(2R: 3S: 4R)-2,3,4,5-tetrahydroxypentanal (Figure 3–9). Given the constitution of xylose and the presence of three asymmetric carbon atoms, (+)-xylose is one of eight possible stereoisomers. Mild oxidation of (+)-xylose gives an optically inactive and therefore *meso*-pentaric acid which must have one of two possible configurations (Figure 2–26B and C). The possible configurations of (+)-xylose are therefore reduced to the following four: (2R: 3S: 4R), (2R: 3R: 4R), and the corresponding enantiomers, (2S: 3R: 4S) and (2S: 3S: 4S). Degradation of (+)-xylose to the lower aldehyde, (−)-threose, followed by mild oxidation, gives (−)-tartaric acid. This establishes the absolute configuration at carbons 3 and 4 of (+)-xylose as (S) and (R), respectively. As shown in Figure 3–9, the configuration of (−)-ribose is similarly established as (2R: 3R: 4R). The sequences discussed also establish the configurations of (−)-threose, (−)-erythrose, xylaric acid, and ribaric acid. The whole family of compounds, which includes higher sugars like (+)-glucose, is related to the secondary configurational standard D-(+)-glyceraldehyde (Exercise 3–14) and is therefore termed D; the enantiomeric series is termed L.

In the configurational correlation of certain atropisomers the question of bond breaking at asymmetric atoms does not arise. The only alternatives are retention of configuration or racemization. Thus, when two of the blocking amino groups in (−)-6,6′-dimethyl-2,2′-biphenyldiamine are replaced by iodine atoms, the product, (+)-6,6′-dimethyl-2,2′-diiodobiphenyl, must still have the corresponding configuration (Formula III):

When bond rupture at the asymmetric carbon is unavoidable, reactions may be resorted to whose stereochemical course is mechanistically understood. Thus, a correlation of lactic acid and alanine (Figure 3–10) is based on the stereochemistry of the transition state in the S_N2 displacement at saturated carbon. This correlation is sound because the product- and rate-determining steps in the S_N2 reaction are one and the same. The stereospecific 1,2-shifts provide further instances of reactions which are under kinetic control. For example, the diazoketone derivative of (R)-hydratropic acid (Figure 3–10) may be rearranged by a 1,2-shift (Wolff rearrangement) into (S)-α-phenethylketene which is hydrolyzed to (S)-homohydratropic acid; similarly the amide or acid azide derivative can be rearranged by the Hofmann and Curtius rearrangements, respectively, to give, after hydrolysis, (R)-α-phenethylamine, and the methyl ketone derivative can be rearranged by the Baeyer-Villiger oxidation to give, after hydrolysis, (R)-α-phenethyl alcohol. In each case the 1,2-shift, whether C → C, C → N or C → O, is completely stereospecific and the migrating α-phenethyl group retains its configuration. Note that (R)-hydratropic acid and (S)-homohydratropic acid have corresponding configurations, even though the configurational notations are opposite (Section 2–5).

In principle, any method which results in optical activation is capable of yielding information on the configuration of the enantiomers, since the conditions which give rise to a difference in the

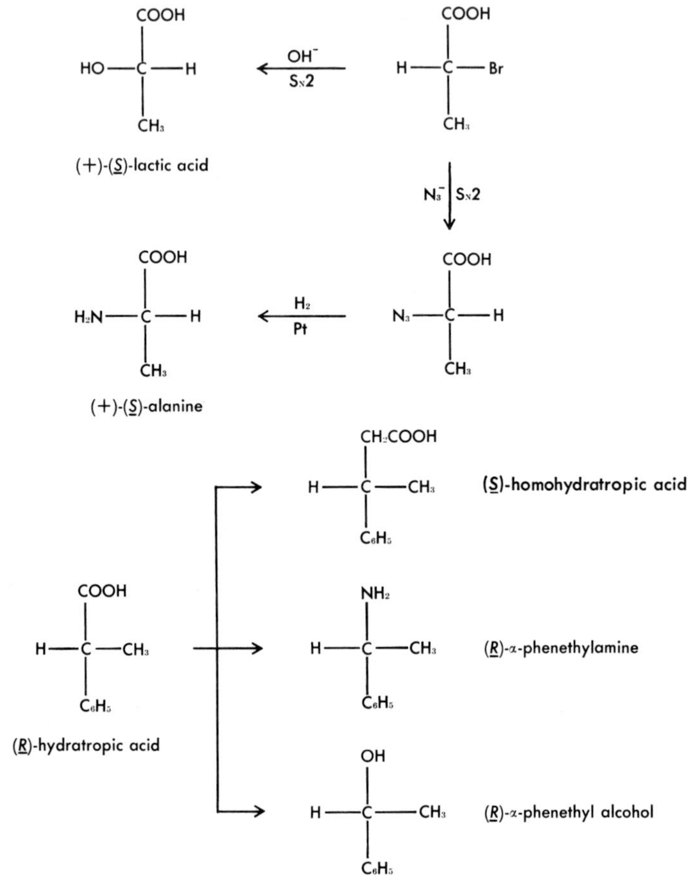

FIGURE 3–10

Configurational correlations involving bond rupture at the asymmetric carbon (Fischer projections).

relative amounts of the enantiomers produced derive in the last analysis from differences in diastereomeric interactions. These differences are in turn reducible to characteristic differences in the molecular shape or topology, and therefore in the configuration, of the molecule. The topology factor which governs the direction of asymmetric syntheses and kinetic resolutions generally resides in secondary forces (e.g., nonbonding and dipole interactions). Thus, in the asymmetric atrolactic acid synthesis (Figure 3–6), the direction of the asymmetric synthesis appears to be governed by

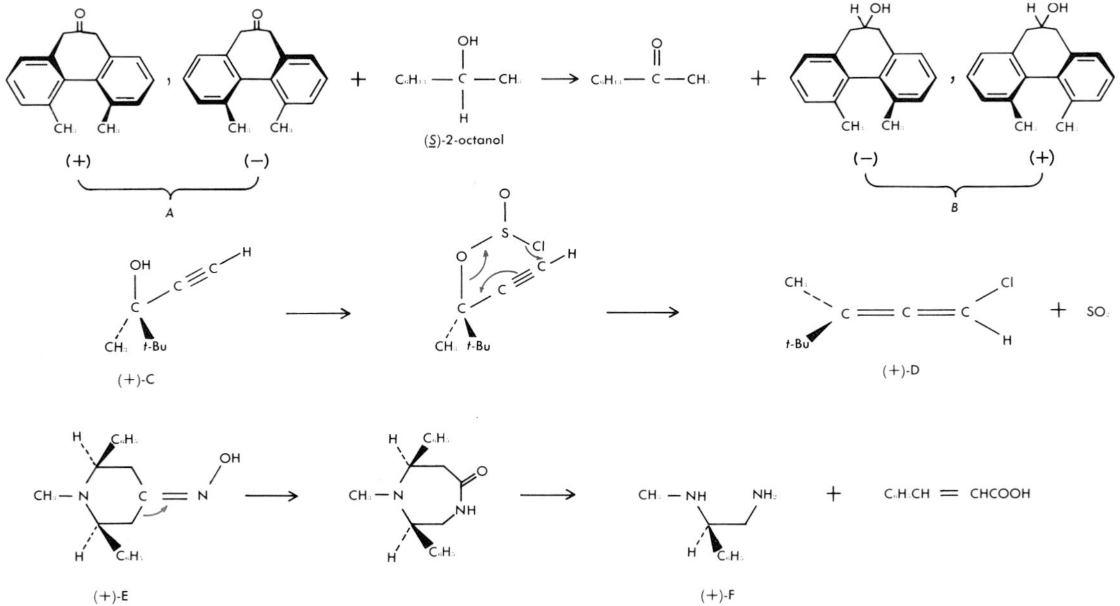

FIGURE 3-11

Configurational correlations involving biphenyls (top), allenes (middle), and geometric enantiomers (bottom).

differences in the free energies of the diastereomeric transition states which arise from differences in nonbonded interactions, as indicated by the observation that for any activating alcohol which has three differently sized residues (S = small, M = medium, L = large) arranged as shown (Formula IV), $(-)$-(R)-atrolactic acid is produced in excess over the enantiomer.

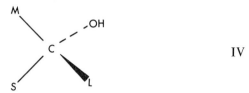

IV

The case of (R)-2-butanol (Figure 3–6) fits this description since $C_2H_5 = L$, $CH_3 = M$, and $H = S$. It is therefore possible to assign configurations to an alcohol by preparing the phenylglyoxylate, reacting this ester with methylmagnesium iodide, and saponifying the product atrolactate: From the sign of the atrolactic acid produced and from a judgment of the relative sizes S, M, and L, the absolute configuration of the alcohol may be deduced.

A variety of chemical methods have been used to correlate the configurations of simple compounds possessing asymmetric carbons with those of less conventional structure. Three examples may suffice (Figure 3–11).

Partial reduction of racemic biphenyl ketone A with (S)-2-octanol (in the presence of aluminum t-butoxide) results in kinetic resolution of A, which becomes enriched in the $(-)$-isomer. At the same time, product alcohol B becomes enriched in $(-)$-B. Lithium aluminum hydride reduction of $(-)$-A gives $(+)$-B. Considerations of nonbonded interactions in the transition state of the asymmetric hydride transfer reaction provide absolute configurational assignments to these biphenyls. Note that in this reaction, as in the partial asymmetric decarboxylation of dl-sec-butylmalonic acid, kinetic resolution (of A) and asymmetric synthesis (of B) take place simultaneously.

Intramolecular rearrangement of the chlorosulfinate ester of alcohol C results in allene D. From the mechanism of the reaction (S_Ni) the stereochemistry of the product may be established.

The absolute configuration of the geometric enantiomer E may be deduced from that of product F which is obtained via Beckmann rearrangement of E. This rearrangement is a stereospecific C → N

1,2-shift which generally proceeds with migration of the group *trans* to the oxime hydroxyl group.

3–6   Configurational Correlations by Physical Methods

X-ray analysis of a crystal structure permits detailed assessment of the relative spatial disposition of the atoms in a molecule. If the molecule contains two (or more) dissymmetric groupings, the relative configurations of these groupings may therefore be directly established. Putting it another way, ordinary X-ray analysis allows direct identification of a given structure as one of a number of possible diastereomers (but not enantiomers). It follows that if the absolute configuration of one of the groupings is known, that of the companion groupings in the molecule can then be ascertained. For example, $(+)$-S-methylcysteine-S-oxide, which is obtained from natural sources (cabbage, turnips), is one of four possible stereoisomers (Figure 3–12). Since a mixture of the same compound and of a diastereomer (but *not* of the enantiomer) is also obtained by oxidation of $(-)$-(R)-S-methylcysteine, it follows that the absolute configuration at the asymmetric carbon is (R). The question of the absolute configuration at the asymmetric sulfur, which could be (R) or (S), was settled by ordinary X-ray diffraction. The structural analysis provided the needed information on the diastereomeric identity. In this manner the absolute configuration at asymmetric sulfur was established as (S).

Other physical methods are also employed in configurational correlations. Unlike X-ray diffraction, these methods are indirect and involve comparisons of molecules whose configurations are known with those of unknown configurations. Although the indirect methods are necessarily less rigorous than X-ray analysis, the correlations which they provide are in most instances unambiguous. Also, in contrast to X-ray diffraction, these methods permit the correlation of a great many configurations in a relatively short period of time and with comparatively simple instrumentation. For this reason, indirect methods play an important role in configurational correlations. Two major types of comparisons have been employed: correlations based on phase relationship in the solid state and correlations based on optical rotatory power.

CORRELATIONS BASED ON PHASE RELATIONSHIPS IN THE SOLID STATE   Phase relationships of enantiomers in the solid state

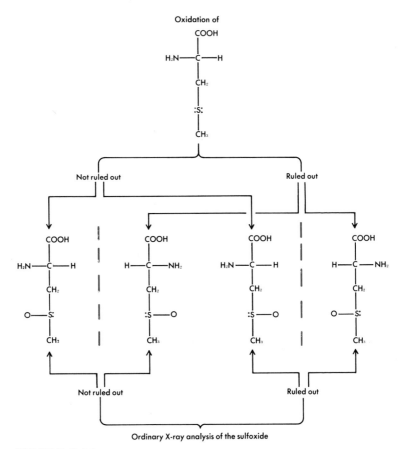

FIGURE 3–12

Absolute configuration at asymmetric sulfur (Fischer projections).

have been briefly discussed in section 2–3. The binary phase diagrams which correspond to the most commonly encountered relationships are shown in Figure 3–13: Conglomerates are simple eutectic mixtures, and racemates are compounds whose melting points generally lie either below or above those of the component enantiomers.

Let us suppose that we have two compounds, *A* and *B,* whose molecules are similar in size and shape. If we remove a molecule of *A* from its crystal lattice, we leave a hole *A′* into which *B* fits snugly. We have formed a solid solution or "mixed crystals." The

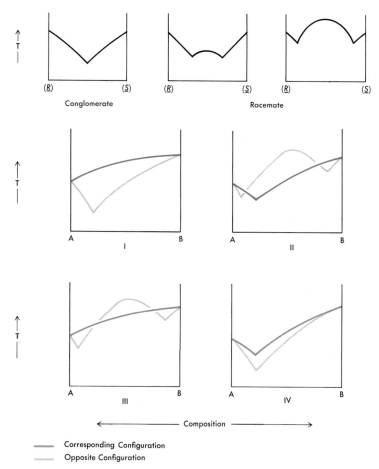

Conglomerate   Racemate

—————— Corresponding Configuration
—————— Opposite Configuration

FIGURE 3–13

Binary phase diagrams (only liquidus curves are shown). The top row shows the most common phase relationships between enantiomers. I–IV, diastereomeric phase relationships between stereoisomers of similar substances A and B.

same is true for the fit of *A* into hole *B'* left by the removal of a molecule of *B* from *its* crystal lattice. *A* and *B* are isomorphous. An example is provided by the solid solutions formed by *p*-toluic and *p*-chlorobenzoic acids, and by *m*-toluic and *m*-chlorobenzoic acids. Mixtures of *p*-toluic and *m*-chlorobenzoic acids on the other hand do *not* form solid solutions.

Now consider the case where A and B are dissymmetric. The hole (R)-A' which is formed by removal of a molecule of (R)-A from its crystal lattice can generally accommodate only (R)-A, but not (S)-A. This selectivity is transferred to the topologically similar B: The hole (R)-A' left by (R)-A will accommodate one enantiomer of B, let us say (R)-B, much more easily than the other, i.e., (S)-B. By the same token, (R)-B' will accommodate (R)-A much more easily than it will accommodate (S)-A. It follows that the isomorphous pair (R)-A and (R)-B, or (S)-A and (S)-B, forms a series of solid solutions while the nonisomorphous pair (R)-A and (S)-B, or (S)-A and (R)-B, does not. It is therefore possible not only to distinguish between enantiomers of B by observing their phase relationships with (R)-A (or (S)-A), but one may also use the characteristic differences in this phase behavior as a basis for assigning configurations to (R)- and (S)-B, relative to that of (R)-A. In the example cited, (R)-A and (R)-B have corresponding configurations whereas (R)-A and (S)-B are *quasi-enantiomers*. These phase relationships are shown in Figure 3–13I and are illustrated by the example in Figure 3–14I.

The above distinction between the enantiomers of B must follow the principles laid down in section 2–1. Accordingly, we note that the two mixtures (R)-$A/(R)$-B and (R)-$A/(S)$-B are diastereomeric, as are the relationships (R)-$A'/(R)$-B and (R)-$A'/(S)$-B.

The conditions for simple solid solution formation may not always be satisfied, yet the phase behavior of the diastereomeric mixtures may still be used to characterize the configurations of the enantiomers of B, using the very principles which we have just discussed. Let us suppose that the enantiomers of A form a pronounced racemate, (R)-$A \cdot (S)$-A. If we remove a molecule of (S)-A from the crystal lattice of the racemate we are left with a hole, (R)-$A \cdot (S)$-A', which will accommodate (S)-B much more easily than (R)-B. The racemate (R)-$A \cdot (S)$-A and the *quasi-racemate* (R)-$A \cdot (S)$-B are now isomorphous. It follows that there exists a tendency toward the formation of an equimolar binary compound between the quasi-enantiomers, (R)-A and (S)-B, but not between the components with corresponding configurations, (R)-A and (R)-B. Compound formation can also be inferred from an examination of the solid state IR spectra and X-ray powder diagrams of the quasi-enantiomeric mixture (R)-$A + (S)$-B, for although the optical properties of the (R)-$A/(R)$-

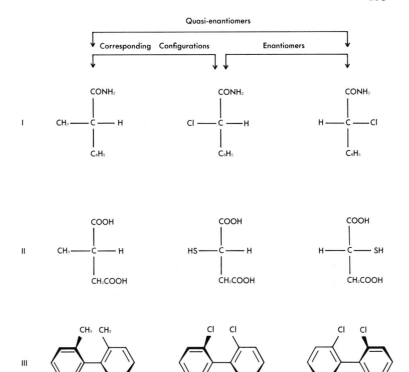

FIGURE 3–14

Some configurational relationships between compounds of similar size and shape, illustrating phase relationships in Figure 3–13.

B mixture should simply be summations of the optical properties of (*R*)-*A* and (*R*)-*B,* quasi-racemate formation would introduce new IR bands and diffraction lines so that the optical properties of (*R*)-*A* · (*S*)-*B* would not likely be summations of the optical properties of (*R*)-*A* and (*R*)-*B* (or (*R*)-*A* and (*S*)-*B*).

These phase relationships are shown in Figure 3–13II and are illustrated by the example in Figure 3–14II. In the ideal case, quasi-racemate formation by the quasi-enantiomers and solid solution formation by the components having corresponding configurations are both observed for the diastereomeric mixtures of the same system; these phase relationships are shown in Figure 3–13III and are illustrated by the example in Figure 3–14III.

Even when isomorphism does not find explicit expression in solid solution or quasi-racemate formation, the diastereomeric mixtures may still show distinctive phase behavior permissive of configurational correlations. Thus, if both mixtures exhibit simple eutectics (Figure 3–13*IV*), the mixture with the lower eutectic temperature consists of the quasi-enantiomeric components, since the tendency toward compound formation is expressed in a greater melting point depression.

CORRELATIONS BASED ON OPTICAL ROTATORY POWER   Comparisons of optical rotations, either at a single wave length or at many, are often suitable for the establishment of a configurational correlation.

Measurements at a single wave length, usually at the D-line, have given rise to two types of monochromatic rules: the rule of *superposition* and the *rule of shift*.

In the rule of superposition it is assumed that the optical rotation of a compound with several dissymmetric groupings is approximately equal to the algebraic sum of the rotations of the constituent groupings. Unfortunately, "rotatory contributions" of dissymmetric groupings cannot be strictly determined because the chemical environment of the groupings varies from molecule to molecule. Even in diastereomers, though the constitution is the same, the environment of a given grouping varies from isomer to isomer both configurationally and conformationally; the intramolecular interactions of dissymmetric groupings are diastereomeric in type and will cause deviations from the calculated sum of group contributions (*vicinal effect*). Nevertheless, granted their approximate nature, appropriate rules have been applied with surprising success, classically in the carbohydrates as Hudson's *rules of isorotation*. In these rules, the anomeric grouping is considered to contribute to the total rotation independently of the rest of the molecule, thus rendering possible a distinction between α- and β-anomers; these rules are a quantitative expression of the observation that the α-anomer of a monosaccharide in the D-series is always more dextrorotatory than the β-anomer.

The rule of shift states that two compounds have corresponding configurations when their molecular rotations undergo parallel changes in direction under changed conditions, including derivatization. This rule has proven wide in scope, a particular example being the Freudenberg *amide rule*. The amide rule plays an important role in the assignment of absolute configurations to α-hydroxy acids (RCHOHCOOH): If the molecular rotation at the D-line is more positive for the derived amide (RCHOHCONH₂) than for the parent acid, the acid has the D-configuration (Sec. 2–5). This aspect of the rule is illustrated in the following Table, in which we have compared the values of $[M]_D$ of three α-hydroxy acids with those of the derived amides. All three acids have the D-configuration.

$[M]_D$ of R—CHOH—COR′

	R		
R′	CH_3 (lactic)	$C_{24}H_{49}$ (cerebronic)	C_6H_{11} (hexahydromandelic)
OH (acid)	− 3°	− 6°	− 40°
NH₂ (amide)	+ 22°	+ 30°	+ 75°

Measurement of optical rotations at many wave lengths provides a great deal more information, since the relationship between molecular structure and optical rotatory power is most advantageously discussed in terms of the sign and magnitude of relevant Cotton effects (Section 2–2). Indeed, comparison of ORD or CD curves has provided a wealth of information on relative and absolute configurations.

If a molecule contains an asymmetrically perturbed symmetric chromophore, such as a nitro or a carbonyl group, the sign of the Cotton effect of such a chromophore is determined by the chirality of the perturbing environment. Since the sign of the Cotton effect reflects the stereochemistry of the environment of the chromophore, it follows that when two comparison substances exhibit curves of the same sign and shape, the configurations of the dissymmetric groupings near the chromophoric groups have corresponding configurations. On the other hand, Cotton effects of opposite sign signalize mirror-image environments and therefore *enantiomeric types*. Thus the chromophore acts as a probe of the chirality of its environment and by comparing the Cotton effect of a compound of known absolute configuration with that of a structurally similar compound, one is in a position to deduce information concerning the absolute configuration and conformation of the latter. An

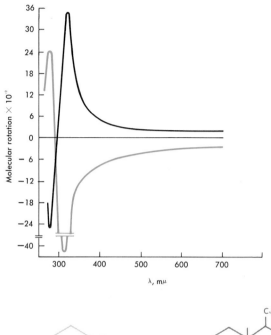

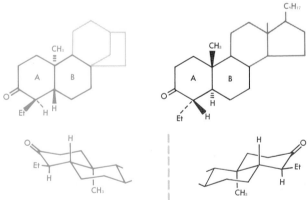

FIGURE 3–15

ORD curves of two ketones whose structures are as shown. Bottom, conformation of the A–B ring portion of the two ketones, showing the mirror-image relationship. The configurations of the two compounds are thus established relative to each other.

example of this type of correlation is shown in Figure 3–15. The two ketones differ structurally, but the immediate environments of the chromophore are enantiomeric. Therefore, oppositely signed $n \rightarrow \pi^*$ Cotton effects are observed. These and many similar obser-

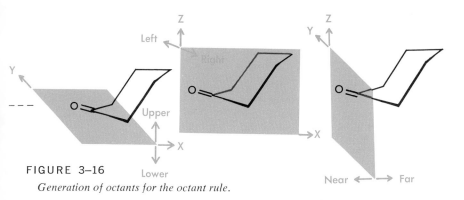

FIGURE 3–16
Generation of octants for the octant rule.

vations have led to a generalization, the *octant rule,* according to which the environment of the carbonyl group is dissected into eight octants, each of which is associated with a sign. The sign of the $n \to \pi^*$ Cotton effect is estimated from the sum of the contributions made by the perturbing groups in each of the eight octants. The division into octants is shown in Figure 3–16 for the case of cyclohexanone. The carbonyl bond axis is made the x-axis, and the observer views the oxygen atom along that axis from the side of the oxygen. A nodal plane passing through the molecule contains the oxygen atom and also carbon atoms 1, 2, and 6; this defines the xy-plane. The xz-plane is a σ plane through carbon atoms 1 and 4, which bisects the carbonyl bond angle. Finally, the yz-plane passes through the carbonyl bond. The octant rule states that atoms lying in the near lower left, near upper right, far lower right, and far upper left octants make positive contributions to the $n \to \pi^*$ Cotton effect, whereas atoms lying in the near lower right, near upper left, far lower left, and far upper right octants make negative contributions. This is easily remembered by noting that no octant of a given sign has a face in common with another octant of the same sign, and, by way of calibration, that the far lower left octant is negative. Atoms or groups which are bisected by any one of the three planes (which then become local σ planes) do not contribute to the sign of the Cotton effect. The student may verify that the observations summarized in Figure 3–15 are in accord with the octant rule.

Even as the chirality of the environment of the carbonyl chromophore has been systematized in the manner just discussed, similar general rules covering other asymmetrically perturbed symmetric chromophores (e.g. nitro) may be formulated. In several cases, comparisons have been made between compounds containing other such chromophores and have empirically led to successful configurational correlations.

If the molecule contains an inherently dissymmetric chromophore, sign and magnitude of the Cotton effect associated with such a chromophore may for all intents and purposes be ascribed entirely to the sense and extent of twist of the chromophore proper.

The contributions to the optical activity attributable to inherent dissymmetry greatly outweigh those that can be attributed to perturbation by asymmetrically disposed substituents. Accordingly, the sign of the Cotton effect will be determined almost solely by the chirality of the inherently dissymmetric chromophore.

Among numerous applications of this concept, two will be selected for discussion: biphenyls and β,γ-unsaturated ketones.

Skewed biphenyls are inherently dissymmetric chromophores. It has been found that the electronic transition which corresponds to the so-called conjugation band in the absorption spectrum is strongly optically active and that the sign of the relevant Cotton effect depends on the chirality of the biphenyl. It has been possible to generalize the relationship between the optical rotatory power and the absolute configuration and conformation of biphenyls in the following rule: A biphenyl whose sense and extent of twist is that shown by the example in Figure 3–17 has a negative Cotton effect of large rotational strength centered at the conjugation band. Sign and magnitude of this Cotton effect are maintained even when other weakly perturbing groups, including those with asymmetric carbon atoms, are present. This generalization permits the correlation of large numbers of compounds containing the biphenyl moiety.

In the case of β,γ-unsaturated ketones, the carbonyl and ethylenic chromophores may couple to form, in combination, a dissymmetric array. Spectroscopically, the principal consequence is a strengthening of the $n \rightarrow \pi^*$ transition and with it a great increase in rotational strength of the associated Cotton effect. In effect, the sign of the $n \rightarrow \pi^*$ Cotton effect in such molecules is determined solely by the orientation of the unsaturated groups with respect to the carbonyl group. Seen in context with the tenets of the octant rule, it

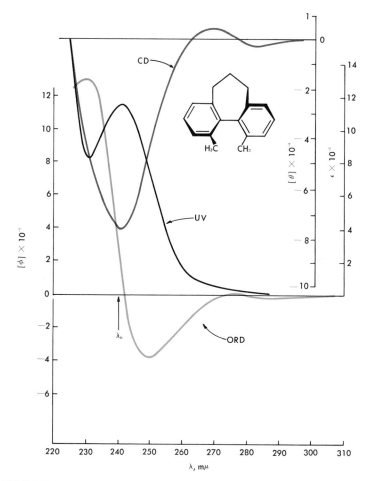

FIGURE 3–17

The relationship between the sense of twist (chirality) and the sign of the Cotton effect of biphenyl, an inherently dissymmetric chromophore, as illustrated for a derivative.

follows that when an olefinic, benzene, or other similar π-system is suitably oriented in a particular far octant, the presence of that π-system is sufficient to determine the sign of the Cotton effect and overrides all other considerations that might arise with regard to contributions by other weakly perturbing groups, including those with asymmetric atoms. Hence, absolute configuration can be

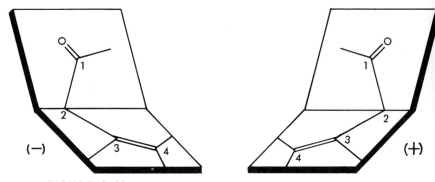

FIGURE 3–18

*Enantiomeric arrangements of the inherently dissymmetric chromophores
associated with some β,γ-unsaturated ketones. The signs refer to the
relevant Cotton effect.*

assigned to a molecule simply by focusing on this composite twisted
chromophore whose chirality is determined by that of the whole
molecular framework in which it is embedded and of which it is an
integral part. Figure 3–18 summarizes the geometric constructs involved.

An important application of these ideas is summarized in Figure
3–19, which shows the $n{\rightarrow}\pi^*$ Cotton effects of the sequiterpene
parasantonide and of (+)-dimethyldibenzsuberone. The two ORD
curves are essentially superimposable and both positive Cotton
effects are extraordinarily intense (for comparison, see Figure
3–15). The identity in the sign of the Cotton effects reflects
identical relative asymmetric dispositions of carbonyl and double-
bond or benzene π-electrons and therefore identical chiralities of
the twisted composite chromophores. Comparison with the construct of Figure 3–18 shows that the chiralities indicated in Figure
3–19 are in harmony with a strong positive Cotton effect. The
absolute configurations thus deduced agree with the results of other
work (Figure 3–11 *A* → *B*). It is noteworthy that although the
sesquiterpene I and the biphenyl II owe their dissymmetry to vastly
dissimilar structural features (the biphenyl is a torsional stereoisomer or atropisomer, whereas the sesquiterpene owes its dissymmetry solely to asymmetric carbon atoms), the chromophore which is
common to both molecules is an unmistakable brand of their absolute configurations: a fitting tribute to the power of this method of
configurational correlation.

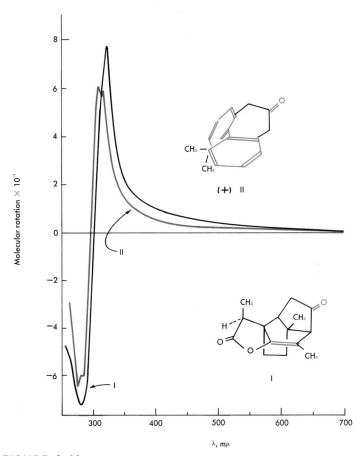

FIGURE 3–19

n→π* Cotton effects of para-*santonide (I) and (+)-dimethyldibenz-suberone (II) in ethanol.*

3–7   Exercises

3–1 2–Thienylglycolic acid (I)   Mandelic acid (II)

Catalytic hydrogenation of (+)-I results in hydrogenolytic cleavage of the carbon-sulfur bonds with desulfurization to give 2-hydroxyhexanoic acid, $[M]_D + 4°$, whose amide has $[M]_D - 25°$. An infrared spectrum and X-ray powder photograph of an equimolar mixture of (−)-I and (−)-II is additively composed of the spectra and lines of the components, whereas a similar mixture of (−)-I and (+)-II gives a different infrared spectrum and powder photograph; in both cases the mixtures were prepared by dissolving the components, mixing the solutions, and evaporating the solution to dryness. By a series of chemical transformations the carboxyl group in (−)-II is reduced to a methyl group. The resulting α-phenethyl alcohol is converted to the phenylglyoxylate ester. Treatment with methylmagnesium iodide, followed by saponification, yields atrolactic acid. What is the sign of rotation of the atrolactic acid, and what are the absolute configurations of (+)-I and (+)-II?

3–2   (*a*) Predict the probable configuration of the predominant isomer of atrolactic acid resulting from the treatment of the pyruvate ($CH_3COCOOR$) of (*S*)-2-butanol with phenylmagnesium iodide, followed by saponification.

(*b*) Would one expect the product resulting from the reaction of 3-phenyl-2-butanone and $^{14}CH_3MgBr$ to be identical with the product resulting from the reaction of 1-^{14}C-3-phenyl-2-butanone and CH_3MgBr?

(*c*) (+)-n-C_6H_{13}-CD(CH_3)OH $\xrightarrow{C_4H_9MgBr}$ ROMgBr + butane
(≡ ROH)
ROMgBr + n-C_3H_7CHO → n-C_3H_7CHDOMgBr + 2-octanone
n-C_3H_7CHDOMgBr + H_2O → (−)-n-C_3H_7CHDOH

Predict the sign of rotation of 1-butanol-1-*d* which is formed from (+)-n-C_6H_{13}-CH(CH_3)OH and butyraldehyde-1-*d*.

trans-methylcinnamate
ester

The *trans*-methylcinnamate ester of (1*S*:2*S*)-bicyclo[2.2.1]heptan-2-ol (ROH) yields an excess of the (*S*)-enantiomer of I. Assuming that this result may be generalized into a LMS-scheme (akin to the scheme of the asymmetric atrolactic acid synthesis), which enantioner of I is produced in excess when the starting ester of bicycloheptanol is (*a*)

(1S:2R), (b) (1R:2S), (c) (1R:2R)? What could be predicted about the relative optical purities of I obtained from the four reactions?

3–4   Dissymmetric and optically active β-methyladipic acid gives two optically active isomeric half-esters with (+)-2-butanol. Will two optically active isomeric half-esters also be obtained from nondissymmetric and optically inactive β-methylglutaric acid and (+)-2-butanol?

3–5   Devise a scheme for obtaining optically pure (+)-α-methylbutyric acid, using as the only active starting material optically pure (−)-α-methylbutyric acid.

3–6

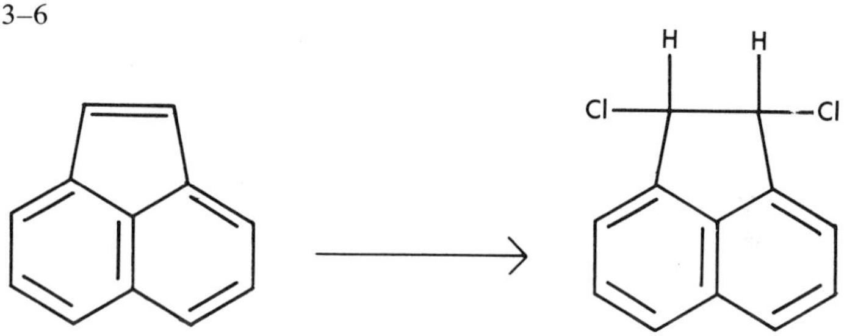

I   II

Treatment of acenaphthene (I) with Cl_2 gives α-II, whereas treatment with iodobenzene dichloride gives a diastereomer, β-II. Identify these isomers given the following information. Each of the isomers was reacted with an insufficient quantity of the optically active base brucine. The α-isomer gave residual II which was optically inactive, whereas the β-isomer gave residual II which was optically active.

3–7

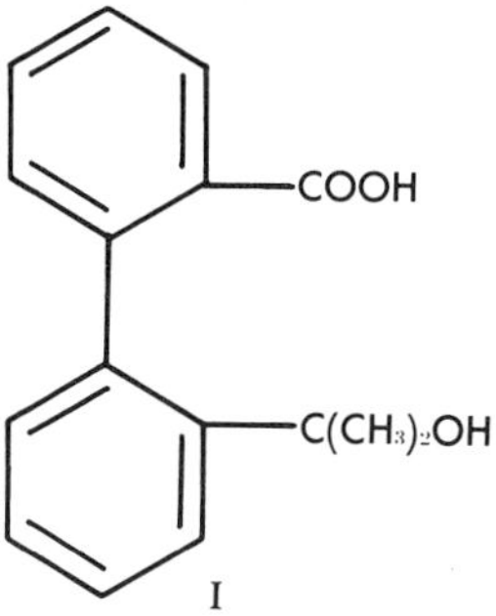

I

Acid I is mixed with one equivalent fo brucine in chloroform at 25°. Directly after mixing, $[a]_{546}$ − 6° (chloroform). Mutarotation occurs, and at equilibrium $[\alpha]_{546} + 2°$.   An equimolar solution of I and brucine in ethanol slowly deposits crystals II, representing 97% of the total amount of I and brucine.   II melts sharply and in chloroform has $[\alpha]_{546} - 50°$ directly after solution.   Mutarotation occurs and at equilibrium $[\alpha]_{546} + 2°$.

(*a*) Are the two rate constants of mutarotation the same?

(*b*) If the mutarotated (equilibrium) solution were to be decomposed with HCl, what would be the optical purity of I at the instant of liberation (approximately)?

(*c*) Upon long standing?

3–8   Optically pure 2-octyl phenyl sulfide was oxidized (with *t*-BuO$_2$H) to a mixture of optically active 2-octyl phenyl sulfoxides *A* (m.p. 20.0–21.5°,$[\alpha]_{546} - 192°$ (ethanol)) and *B* (m.p. $- 3.7$ to $- 2.2°$, $[\alpha]_{546} + 173°$ (ethanol)).   When sufoxide *A* was heated with potassium *t*-butoxide in dimethyl sulfoxide, epimerization occurred at carbon but not at sulfur.   When equilibrium was reached, the equilibrium mixture *X* was isolated and oxidized (H$_2$O$_2$) to 2-octyl phenyl sulfone which had $[\alpha]_{546} + 3.3°$ (chloroform).   Direct oxidation (H$_2$O$_2$) of *A* afforded sulfone with $[\alpha]_{546} + 14.5°$ (chloroform).   Control experiments demonstrated that oxidation of known mixtures of the diastereomeric sulfoxides produced sulfone whose rotation accurately measured the ratios of the diastereomeric starting materials. Calculate $[\alpha]_{546}$ of the mixture *X* in ethanol.

3–9

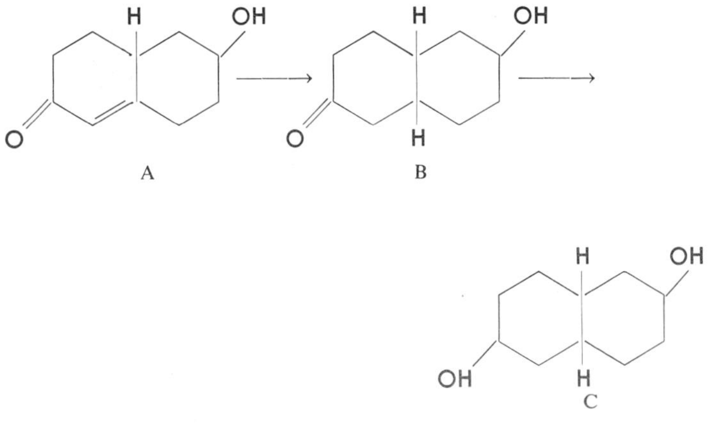

Two compounds I and II differing in infrared spectrum and melting point have structure *A*. I was reduced to a separable mixture of III and IV whereas II was reduced to a separable mixture of V and VI. All four products have constitution *B*. III was reduced to a separable mixture of VII and VIII (constitution *C*), IV to a separable mixture of IX and X (constitution *C*), V to a separable mixture of XI and XII (constitution *C*), and VI to a separable mixture of VIII and XIII (constitution *C*). All separations were performed by fractional crystallization or by chromatography on silica or alumina. All compounds except VII and XIII were optically active. X and XII were identical in: m.p. R_f, UV, IR, NMR spectra, dipole moment, solubility, but the mixture m.p. was depressed. Assign configurations to I–XIII which are consistent with the given information.

3–10

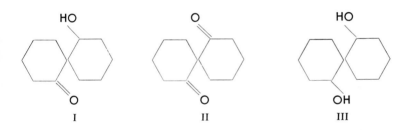

I II III

Compound I, prepared from optically inactive precursors, was separated by chromatography on alumina into two compounds, α-I and β-I, each of which was resolved. Mild oxidation of (+)-β-I gave (+)-II. Lithium aluminum hydride reduction of (−)-α-I or (−)-β-I gave III. The product of reduction (−)-α-I was separated by chromatography on silica gel into (−)-α-III and (+)-β-III. Similarly, the reduction product from (−)-β-I was separable into (+)-α-III and (+)-γ-III. Would mild oxidation of (+)-α-I give (+)- or (−)-II? Draw structures for the isomers of III which are consistent with this information.

3–11 Consider the decarboxylation of *dl-sec*-butyl-malonic acid (*A*) to 3-methylpentanoic acid (*B*) in the presence of brucine and show that the following relationship obtains at any time during the decarboxylation: $O_A X_A = O_B X_B$, where X_A and X_B are the total quantities of the substances and O_A and O_B their optical purities. When is the maximum optical enrichment of *A* achieved?

3–12 (*a*) What is the sign of the conjugation band Cotton effect (i) of *A* in Figure 1–16 and (ii) of II in Figure 3–19? (*b*) Applying the tenets of the octant rule, predict the sign of the $n \rightarrow \pi^*$ Cotton effect of (i) (*R*)-3-methylcyclohexanone, (ii) (*S*)-2-methylcyclohexanone, (iii) dehydrocamphor (formula shown).

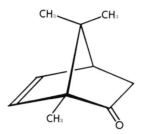

3–13   In an equilibrium mixture of conformers, such as axial and equatorial 3-methylcyclohexanone, show that the following relationship obtains, where R_a, R_e, C_a and C_e stand for the rotational strengths (R) and concentrations (C) of the axial and equatorial forms, and R_m for the rotational strength of the mixture:

$$\frac{C_e}{C_a} = \frac{R_a - R_m}{R_m - R_e}$$

Could physical properties other than R also have been chosen, such as specific rotation at a given wave length or chemical shift of a particular hydrogen nucleus?

3–14   When D-(+)-glyceraldehyde is treated with hydrogen cyanide and the resulting cyanohydrin is hydrolyzed, two 2,3,4-trihydroxybutanoic acids A and B are formed. Acid A is identical with the acid obtained by mild oxidation of $(-)$-threose. Name the configurations of $(+)$-glyceraldehyde and of the two acids.

3–15   The enzymatic decarboxylation of L-tyrosine ($C_6H_5CH_2$-CH(NH$_2$)COOH) in D$_2$O yields (R)-α-^{2}H-tyramine (C_6H_5-CH$_2$CHD-NH$_2$). Did the replacement of the carboxyl group by deuterium proceed with retention or inversion of configuration, "retention" signifying that starting material and product have the same configuration at the grouping common to both ($C_6H_5CH_2CH(NH_2)$-)?

3–16   Paper chromatography of a *dl*-pair sometimes results in a separation of the enantiomers. Explain.

3–17   In the asymmetric atrolactic acid synthesis, unless the mixture of atrolactates (which is obtained on addition of methylmagnesium iodide to phenylglyoxylate) is *completely* saponified, one may come to erroneous conclusions concerning the absolute configuration of the activating alcohol. How is this possible?

3–18   Classify the following stereochemical reactions according to types 1 or 2 (Figure 3–1).

(a)

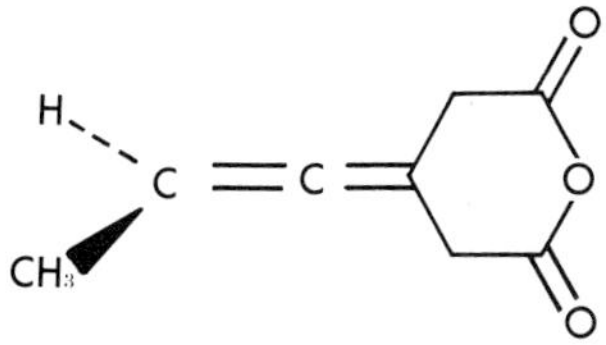

 + (i) CH₃OH, (ii) (R)-2-butanol

(b) Semihydrogenation of (C₂H₅) (CH₃) CH — C ≡ CH

(c)   (i)

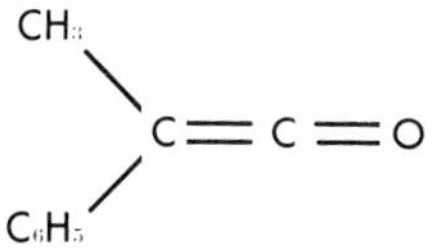

in the presence of optically active acetylquinine. (ii) Is the product optically active methyl hydratropate?

(d) Reaction of optically active diisopinocampheylborane with (i) butanone, to give optically active 2-butanol, (ii) *cis*-2-butene, to give optically active 2-butanol after oxidative cleavage of the adduct.

(e)

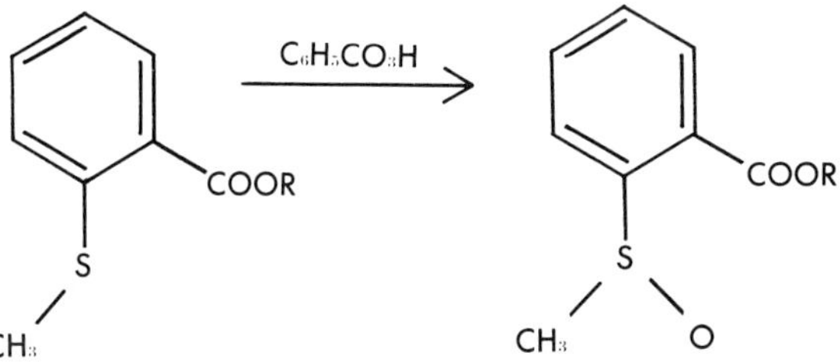

(f) Treatment of *dl*-hydratropoyl chloride (i) with an insufficient quantity of (R)-2-butanol and (ii) with an excess of (R)-2-butanol. (iii) Will complete saponification of the product ester (2-butyl hydratropate) give optically active hydratropic acid?

(g) Reduction of *dl-nor*camphor with (i) lithium aluminum hydride; (ii) diisopinocampheylborane.

(h) Partial decomposition of *dl*-2-butanol over nickel deposited on optically active quartz at 550° (residual alcohol is optically active).

(i) Partial hydrolysis of N-acetyl-*dl*-alanine in the presence of hog-kidney acylase to give L-alanine and N-acetyl-D-alanine.

3–19   In the presence of an enzyme dehydrogenase, one enantiomer of stearic acid-9-³H gives oleic acid-9-³H whereas the other enantiomer gives oleic acid-9-¹H. Comment on this result.

3–20   The *isotope dilution technique* is one of the most reliable methods for establishing the optical purity of a sample. In its simplest application, an unlabeled sample of the substance is partly resolved to give material of specific rotation α_o. To y g. of this sample there is now added x g. of racemic, labeled substance ("carrier") having specific radioactivity C_o. The mixture is reresolved or optically fractionated by recrystallization to give material with a new specific rotation α and a new specific radioactivity C. The weight E of enantiomer in excess over racemate in the starting sample is then given by

$$E^2 = \frac{y\,[(x+y)^2 - (C_o x/C)\,(x+y)]}{y - (C_o x/C)\,(\alpha/\alpha_o)}$$

Problem: 5.2645 g. of a nonradioactive, partly resolved acid, $[\alpha]_D +$ 7.73° (chloroform), was mixed with 1.0088 g. of radioactive racemic acid, 1280 counts/min/mg. The mixture was crystallized with brucine. From the mother liquors there was obtained (after decomposition of the salt) 0.7 g. of acid, $[\alpha]_D + 11.75°$ (chloroform), 198 counts/min/mg. Calculate the specific rotation of the optically pure acid.

■ ANSWERS TO EXERCISES

1–1   (a) 101.5°, sp⁵. Note the analogy with two distorted tetrahedra sharing a common face, even as the τ-bond description of ethylene has its analogy in two distorted tetrahedra sharing a common edge. (b) 109.5°, sp³.

1–3   In the dimethyl compound the reactive X groups are brought closer together than in the parent compound; consider the effect of nonbonded repulsive interactions on bond angles and conformer population.

1–4 $\mathbf{D}_{5h}$, $\mathbf{D}_{5d}$ and $\mathbf{D}_5$. Yes. No. Five.

1–5   (a) Derivatives of $\mathbf{D}_{4h}$: $\mathbf{C}_s$, $\mathbf{C}_{2v}$, $\mathbf{D}_{2h}$.
       Derivatives of $\mathbf{D}_{2d}$: $\mathbf{C}_s$, $\mathbf{C}_s$, $\mathbf{C}_{2v}$.
(b) ca. 20 kcal/mole if $\Delta\theta = 22°$.

1–6   Acidity series cyclopropane > cyclobutane > cyclopentane since the s-character of the carbon AO's in the C—H bonds decreases in the order of increasing C—C—C internuclear angle.

1–8   Symmetries: $\mathbf{C}_{2v}$, $\mathbf{D}_{3h}$, $\mathbf{D}_2$ (dissymmetric!), $\mathbf{T}_d$.
       Lengths: 3,2,4,1.   Angles: 4,2,5,2.

1–9   (a) 120°, 0.2 kcal/mole; 132°, 3 kcal/mole.
(b) 83°; 102°, 2 kcal/mole; 122°, 0.4 kcal/mole.   In the acyclic series, the increasing spread in the bond angle results from increasing nonbonded interaction.

1–10   (a) One eclipsed $\mathbf{C}_s$ conformation, one staggered $\mathbf{C}_s$ conformation, an infinite number of $\mathbf{C}_1$ conformations.

169

(b) Six. No.

1–11   (a) 3.2 Å, 0.15 kcal/mole net attractive energy.
(b) 2.5 Å.

1–12 σ-framework $= 10\ sp^2 + 4\ sp$ carbons; π-framework $= 14$ π-electrons whose nodal plane is the σ-framework $+ 4$ π-electrons at right angles to the other 14 and centered on the sp carbons.

1–13   (a) $\mathbf{C}_{xv}$ and $\mathbf{D}_{xh}$.   (b) No; e.g., methylacetylene $(\mathbf{C}_{3v})$ has no torsional barriers.

1–14   (a) 125, 167, 250 cps.
(b) 102.5°, 107.6°, 107.0°, 108.8°, 109.7°, 111.0°. Note that the *internuclear* C—C—C angles are 60°, 89.3°, 90°, 103.3°, 109.7° and 116°.

1–15   (a) $\mathbf{C}_s$, $\mathbf{C}_{2h}$, $\mathbf{C}_{4v}$, $\mathbf{D}_{2d}$.
(b) $\mathbf{C}_1$, $\mathbf{C}_2$, $\mathbf{C}_4$, $\mathbf{D}_2$.
(c) $\mathbf{C}_1$ only.
(d) $\mathbf{C}_1$, $\mathbf{C}_2$, $\mathbf{C}_s$, $\mathbf{C}_{2v}$, $\mathbf{C}_{2h}$, $\mathbf{S}_2$, $\mathbf{S}_4$.

1–17   Three mutually perpendicular C_4, four C_3, six C_2, nine σ.

1–18   (a)–(d) False; (e) and (f) True.

2–1   A. 5 *meso* diastereomers, no optical isomers; B. 2 *dl*-pairs $(= 4$ optical isomers); C. 2 *meso*-diastereomers plus 4 *dl*-pairs $(= 8$ optical isomers); D. 3 *dl*-pairs plus 1 *meso*-form; E. No isomers for a-a and a-b; 1 *dl*-pair for b-b: F. 2 diastereomers (*cis* and *trans*), no optical isomers; for an analog of the *trans*-form, see Figure 2–28; G. 1 *dl*-pair; H. 3 *dl*-pairs; I. 3 diastereomeric *dl*-pairs; J. One *dl*-pair; K. One *dl*-pair plus 1 *meso* form; L. 4 *dl*-pairs plus 2 *meso* forms; M. 2 *dl*-pairs plus 1 *meso*-form; N. 6 *meso*-forms (no optical isomers); O. 2 *dl*-pairs plus 2 *meso*-forms; P. 1 *dl*-pair, 5 *meso*-forms; Q. 3 *dl*-pairs.

2–2   The asymmetric *dl*-pair.

2–3   Enantiomers, since diastereomers do not absorb at exactly the same wave length.

2–4   A, B, H, and K are (a); all others are (b).

2–5   (a) 2-Butanol, 2-butene, *trans*-1,2-dimethylcyclopropane.
(b) (i) cyclobutene-3-carboxylic acid, (ii) buta-1,2-diene-1-carboxylic acid, (iii) 2-ethyl-3-butynoic acid, or penta-1,2-diene-1-carboxylic acid or penta-2,3-diene-1-carboxylic acid, (iv) 2- or 3-pentenoic acid, (v) 2-methyl-2-butenoic acid, (vi) 2-methyl-3-butenoic acid, (vii) 2-ethylpropenoic acid.

2–6   Buttressing of the 2′-group by the 3′-group.

2–7   They are opposite, i.e., one is (R) and the other (S). Hence at high temperatures, when the interconversion of the conformational enantiomers is very rapid, this is a classical *meso*-form; compare with the case of *cis*-1,2-dimethylcyclohexane, Figure 2–30.

2–8   (heavy dot means hydrogen up, otherwise down)

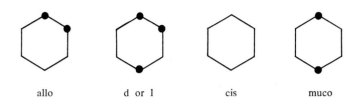

allo   d or l   cis   muco

2–9   (1) *meso-cis-syn-cis* (*ea-aa-ae*). (2) *dl-cis-syn-trans* or *cis-anti-trans* (*ae-ee-ee*). (3) *meso-cis-anti-cis* (*ea-ae-ea*); the molecule undergoes degenerate interconversion. (4) *meso-trans-syn-trans* (*ee-ee-ee*). (5) *dl-trans-anti-trans* (*aa-ae-ee* is impossible, therefore the center ring is in the twist form).

2–10   The four stereoisomers are dissymmetric and form two *dl*-pairs. Each isomer has one enantiomer and two diastereomers. Any pair of diastereomers also constitutes a pair of geometric isomers.

2–11   (*a*) 1,1- and *cis*-1,4-isomer: two conformational disastereomers.

(*b*) *cis*-1,2-, *cis*-1,3- and *trans*-1,3-isomers: configurational *dl*-pairs and conformational diastereoisomers.

2–12   (*A*) 8; (*B*) 4; (*C*) 8; (*D*) 4.

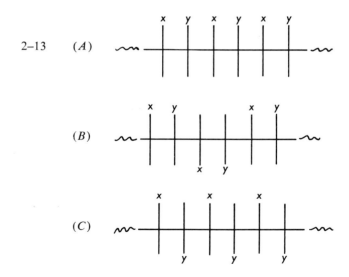

2–13   (*A*)

(*B*)

(*C*)

2–15   Isopropyl methyl groups in C and D.
2–16   (5*R*:6*S*:9*R*:13*S*:14*R*)

2–17   (b) 4 dl-pairs, (c) 6 dl-pairs, (d) 4 dl-pairs plus 6 meso-forms.

2–18   All thianthrene 5,10-dioxides exist in the form of cis- and trans-isomers which are configurationally stable at room temperature.

(a) The isomer may be a meso-form which is a mixture of non-dissymmetric conformational diastereomers (analogy: cis-1,3- and trans-1,4-dimethylcyclohexanes). This is the case with cis-unsubstituted, cis-1,4-, cis-2,3-, and trans-1,9-, and cis- and trans-2,8-disubstituted isomers.

(b) The isomer may be a meso-form which consists of a single non-dissymmetric conformer undergoing degenerate interconversion (analogy: cis-1,4-dimethylcyclohexane). This is the case with the trans-unsubstituted isomer.

(c) The isomer may be a dl-pair, each component of which consists of an equilibrium mixture of dissymmetric conformational diastereomers (analogy: trans-1,2-dimethylcyclohexane). This is the case with cis- and trans-monosubstituted, cis- and trans-1,2-, 1,3-, 1,7 and 1,8-disubstituted, cis-1,6- and cis-2,7-disubstituted isomers.

(d) The isomer may be a dl-pair, each component of which consists of a single dissymmetric conformer undergoing degenerate interconversion (analogy: trans-1,3-dimethylcyclohexane). This is the case with the trans-1,4- and trans-2,3-disubstituted isomers.

(e) The isomer may be a meso-form which consists of a conformational dl-pair (analogy: cis-1,2-dimethylcyclohexane; Exercise 2–7). This is the case with trans-1,6- and trans-2,7-disubstituted isomers.

2–19   By a $[\alpha]_D$ such as $-4000°$ or $+5000°$.

2–20   (a) The all-trans form.

(b) $\mathbf{C}_1$, $\mathbf{C}_s$, $\mathbf{C}_{3v}$, $\mathbf{C}_{4v}$, $\mathbf{D}_{2h}$, $\mathbf{T}_d$.

2–21   The trans-1,3,3,4,6,6-hexamethyl isomer.

3–1   Dextrorotatory; (+)-I is (R) and (+)-II is (S).

3–2   (a) (R); (b) no; (c) dextrorotatory.

3–3   (a) (R); (b) (S); (c) (R). The optical purities of I obtained from (a) and (b) are the same, and those of I from (c) and (1S:2S)-ROH are the same, but the values for the two sets are different in principle.

3–4   Yes.

3–5   Racemize a portion of the (−)-acid (ester + sodium ethoxide). Convert a portion of the (−)-acid to optically active amine via a C → N 1,2-shift reaction. Resolve dl-acid with the amine.

3–6   α-II is the meso- and β-II the dl-isomer.

3–7   (a) The rates are the same; (b) 18%; (c) 0%.

3–8 $-185°$.

3–9   (for one enantiomer)

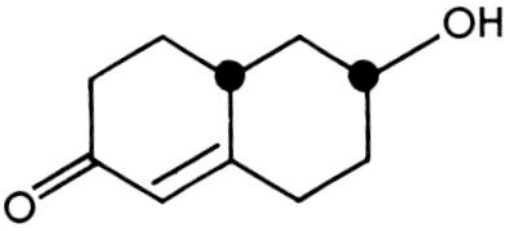

I

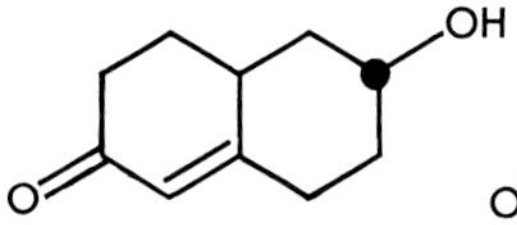

II 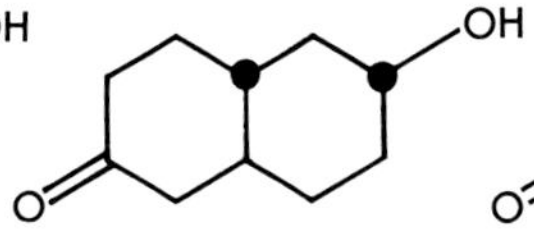   III 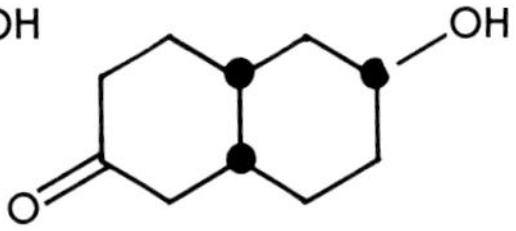   IV

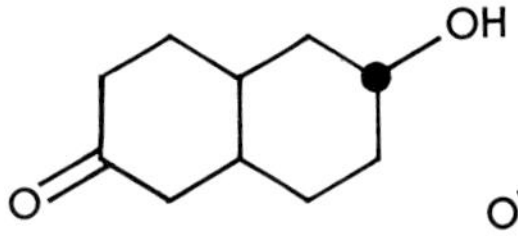

V 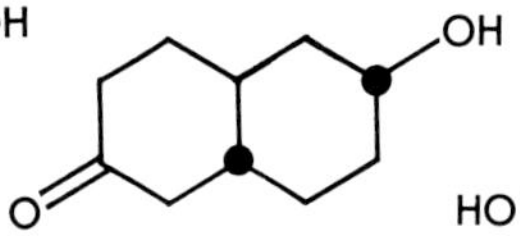   VI 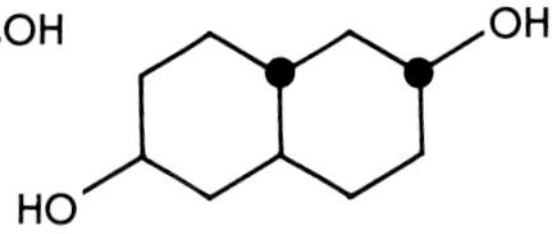   VII

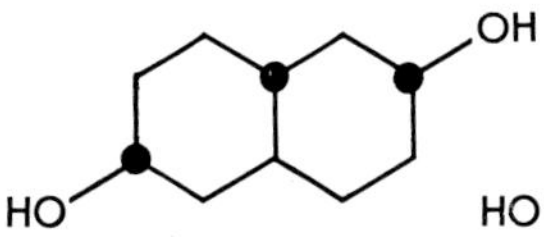

VIII 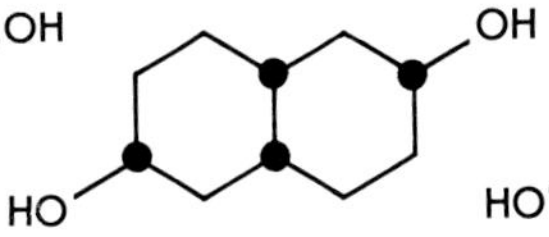   IX 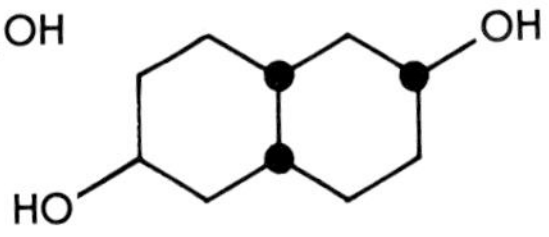   X

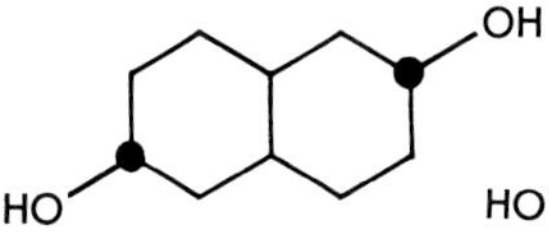

XI 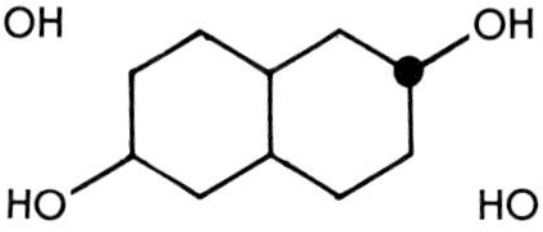   XII 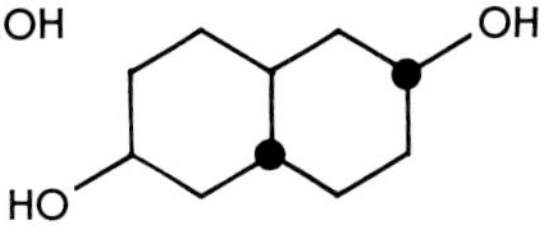   XIII

3–10   (−)-II.   The isomers of III are, for example: OH

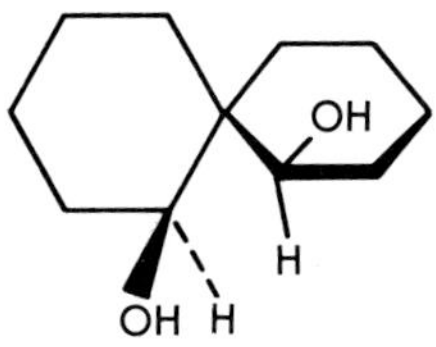

(−)-α-III 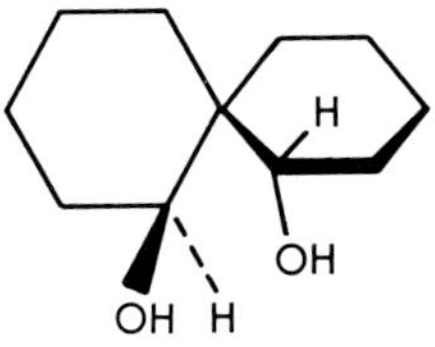   (+)-β-III 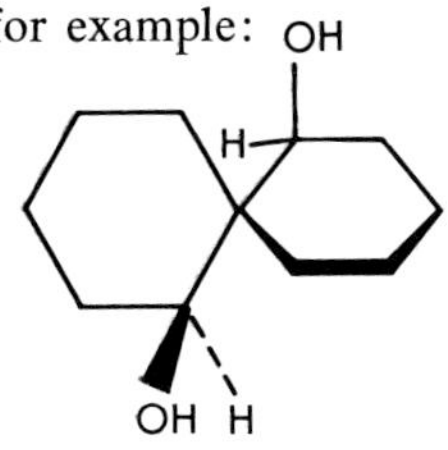   (+)-γ-III

3–11   At $t = \infty$.

3–12   (*a*) (i) and (ii): positive.   (*b*) (i): positive because in most molecules the methyl group is equatorial; (ii): positive because only molecules with axial methyl groups contribute to the Cotton effect in chair-cyclohexane.   (iii): negative according to Figure 3–18.

3–13   Yes.

3–14   (*R*)-glyceraldehyde; *A* is (2*S*:3*R*); *B* is (2*R*:3*R*).

3–15   Retention.

3–16   Cellulose is dissymmetric.

3–17   The absolute configuration is deduced from the sign of rotation of the atrolactic acid.   This in turn depends on the ratio (*R*)/(*S*) which may be greater or less than unity.   This ratio is equal to the ratio of the two atrolactates.   However, since these atrolactates are diastereomers, their rates of saponification are different so that, if the saponification is incomplete, the predominant enantiomer of atrolactic acid does not necessarily derive from the more abundant diastereomer but rather from the *more reactive* diastereomer, and this may well be the *less abundant* form!

3–18   (*a*)i is la; (*a*)ii, (*c*)i, (*d*)i and (*d*)ii are 2a; (*b*), (*e*) and (*g*)i are 2b; (*f*)i, (*f*)ii, (i), and possibly (*h*) are 2c; (*h*) may be 2d; (*g*)ii is 2d.   (*c*)ii: only if the reaction is not allowed to go to completion.   (*f*)iii: ditto, i.e., only under the conditions of (*f*)i.

3–19   C-9 is a *meso* carbon atom and, since the enzyme is dissymmetric, only one of the methylene hydrogens is biologically labile.

3–20   30°.

■ BIBLIOGRAPHY

General Texts Covering Much of the Material in This Book and Containing References to the Original Literature

E. L. ELIEL, *Stereochemistry of Carbon Compounds,* McGraw-Hill, New York, 1962.

K. FREUDENBERG, *Stereochemie, F.* Deuticke, Leipzig and Vienna, 1932.

W. KLYNE, *Progress in Stereochemistry,* Academic Press, New York, 1954, Vol. I, and subsequent volumes with P. B. D. DE LA MARE: Vol. II (1958) and Vol. III (1962).

R. L. SHRINER, R. ADAMS and C. S. MARVEL, Chapter 4 in Vol. I of H. GILMAN, *Organic Chemistry,* 2nd ed., John Wiley & Sons, New York, 1943.

G. W. WHELAND, *Advanced Organic Chemistry,* 3rd ed., John Wiley & Sons, New York, 1960, or earlier editions of this classic text.

Suggestions for Additional Reading on Selected Topics

Symmetry elements and point groups

F. A. COTTON, *Chemical Applications of Group Theory,* Interscience, New York, 1963; H. H. JAFFÉ and M. ORCHIN, *Theory and Applications of Ultraviolet Spectroscopy,* John Wiley & Sons, New York, 1962, Chapter 4; G. HERZBERG, *Molecular Spectra and Molecular Structure,* D. Van Nostrand Co., Inc., Princeton, 1945; H. H. JAFFÉ and M. ORCHIN, *Symmetry in Chemistry,* John Wiley & Sons, New York, 1965; M. GARDNER, *The Ambidextrous Universe,* Basic Books, New York, 1964.

Hybridization and bent bonds

C. A. COULSON, *Valence,* Oxford University Press, 1st ed. (1952) or 2nd ed. (1961), Chapter 8; M. J. S. Dewar, ed., *An Epistologue on Carbon Bonds, Tetrahedron,* **17**, 125–266 (1962); K. MISLOW, *Tetrahedron Letters,* 1415 (1964).

Molecular deformations

F. H. WESTHEIMER, in Chapter 12 of M. S. NEWMAN, *Steric Effects in Organic Chemistry,* John Wiley & Sons, New York, 1956.

Classification of stereoisomers

W. K. NOYCE, *J. Chem. Ed.,* **38**, 23 (1961). See also G. W. WHELAND, *loc. cit.,* chapter 6.9–6.10.

Chemical topology

H. L. FRISCH and E. WASSERMAN, *J. Am. Chem. Soc.,* **83**, 3789 (1961); E. WASSERMAN, *Scientific American,* **207**, 94 (1962); G. SCHILL and A. LÜTTRINGHAUS, *Angew. Chem.,* **76**, 567 (1964).

Structure and optical activity

C. DJERASSI, *Optical Rotatory Dispersion,* McGraw-Hill, New York, 1960, especially Chapter 12 by A. MOSCOWITZ; Proceedings of a Conference on Optical Rotatory Dispersion (held in 1960 at The Inn, Rancho Santa Fe, California),

Tetrahedron, **13,** 1–240 (1961); K. Mislow, *Ann. N.Y. Acad. Sci.,* **93,** 457 (1962); S. F. MASON, "Optical Rotatory Power," *Quart. Revs.* (London), **17,** 20 (1963); P. CRABBÉ, *Optical Rotatory Dispersion and Circular Dichroism in Organic Chemistry,* Holden-Day, San Francisco, 1965; L. VELLUZ, M. LEGRAND and M. GROSJEAN, *Optical Circular Dichroism,* Academic Press, New York, 1965; T. M. LOWRY, *Optical Rotatory Power,* Dover Publications, New York, 1964.

Asymmetric syntheses and optical resolutions

J. I. KLABUNOWSKI, *Asymmetrische Synthese,* Deutscher Verlag der Wissenschaften, Berlin, 1963; W. THEILACKER, in HOUBEN-WEYL, *Methoden der Organischen Chemie,* Thieme Verlag, Stuttgart, 1955, Part 4/2, p. 505 ff.

Topics of historical interest

J. H. VAN'T HOFF, *The Arrangements of Atoms in Space,* 2nd ed., (transl. A. Eiloart), Longmans, Green, London, 1898; F. M. JAEGER, *Spatial Arrangements of Atomic Systems and Optical Activity,* McGraw-Hill, New York, 1930; F. M. JAEGER, *Lectures on the Principles of Symmetry,* Elsevier, Amsterdam, 1917.

Fluxional Structures

W. VON E. DOERING and W. R. ROTH, *Tetrahedron,* **19,** 715–737 (1963).

Specification of Absolute Configuration

R. S. CAHN, *J. Chem. Ed.,* **41,** 116 (1964).

Meso Carbon Atoms

H. HIRSCHMANN, in S. GRAFF, ed., *Essays in Biochemistry,* John Wiley & Sons, New York, 1956.

Conformational Analysis

E. L. ELIEL, N. L. ALLINGER, S. J. ANGYAL and G. A. MORRISON, *Conformational Analysis,* Interscience, New York, 1965; M. HANACK, *Conformation Theory,* Academic Press, New York, 1965.

■ INDEX

Absolute asymmetric synthesis, 139
Absolute configuration, 94
  and asymmetric atoms, 94
  by X-ray analysis, 142
  rotation, 94–96
  see also Configurational corre-
    lation
Acenaphthene dichloride, stereoisomers, 163
Acetaldehyde, asymmetric reduction,
  129, 137
  torsional barrier, 36
Acetone, bond angle, 48
Acetyl chloride, bond angles, 9
Acetylene, linearity, 7
  acid strength, 47
  bent bonds, 46
  bond lengths, 7, 8
  cylindrical symmetry, 7, 32
  geometry in excited state, 41
Acyclic hydrocarbons, bond angles,
  12, 17
Adamantane, point group, 47
Alanine, absolute configuration, 145

Allenes, bonding, 22
  absolute configuration, 147, 148
  asymmetric (C_1), 167
  condition for enantiomerism, 85
  dissymmetric (C_2), 27
  geometry, 22
  unsubstituted (D_{2d}), 32
Alternating axis of symmetry
  see Rotation-reflection axis
Amide rule, 154
α-Amino acids, configuration, 96,
  106, 145
Ammonia, threefold axis of symmetry, 4
  C_{3v} symmetry, 30
  planes of symmetry, 4
Amplitude of ORD curve, 60
Angle bending
  see Bond angle bending
Angle strain, 35
  in racemization of biphenyls, 79
  as reflected in molecular models,
    43
  relation to internuclear angle, 35

in small bicyclic systems, 101
Anhydrides, stereochemistry of alco-
    holysis, 124–126
Anomalous X-ray scattering, 142
Anomer, 91, 154
Ansa compounds, atropisomerism,
    81
Anti-conformations, 37, 38
    and conformational isomerism, 70
Antipodes
    see Enantiomers
Arachidonic acid, isomers, 84
Asymmetric atoms, 87
Asymmetric atrolactic acid synthesis,
    132–134, 146, 148, 162, 166,
    173
Asymmetric carbon atom, 25
    and C_1 symmetry, 26
    and C_2 symmetry, 25, 28
    condition for presence, 90, 116
    and isomer number, 88
    notation of absolute configuration,
        94–96
    in poly-(R)-propylene oxide, 106
    and stereoisomerism, 86–102
    in tactic polymers, 103–104
Asymmetric catalysis, 129, 134, 139
Asymmetric conformations, point
    group, 25
Asymmetric decarboxylation of *sec*-
    butylmalonic acid, 139
Asymmetric degradation of citric
    acid, 137–138
Asymmetric dehydration of olefins,
    167
Asymmetric dehydrogenation of
    stearic acid, 167
Asymmetric destruction, 136–139
Asymmetric hydration of fumaric
    acid, 141
Asymmetric hydrolysis of amides,
    167
Asymmetric induction
    see Asymmetric synthesis
Asymmetric nitrogen atom, 87, 88
Asymmetric phosphorylation of
    glycerol, 129
Asymmetric reduction of aldehydes

and ketones, 129, 131–134, 167
Asymmetric reduction of olefins,
    162, 167
Asymmetric sulfur atom, 88
    see also Sulfoxides
Asymmetric synthesis, 128, 140
    absolute, 139
    atrolactic acid, 132–134, 146, 148,
        162, 166, 173
    and configurational correlations,
        145–148
    conservative, 131
    self-immolative, 131
Asymmetric transformation, total,
    121
    second order, 122, 164
Asymmetrically perturbed symmetric
    chromophores, 65
    in configuration correlations, 155–
        160
Asymmetry, 25
    and the asymmetric carbon atom,
        26
    in conical and cylindrical helices,
        26, 28
    in helical biopolymers, 26
    in twisted biphenyls, 26
Atactic polymers, 104
Atomic asymmetry
    see Asymmetric atoms, Asymmet-
        ric carbon
Atomic orbitals, overlap, 13
    carbon, 13
    hydrogen, 13
Atrolactic acid synthesis, asymmetric
    see Asymmetric atrolactic acid
        synthesis
Atropisomers, 78–81
Axial bonds in cyclohexane, 77, 78
Axis of rotation:
    see Axis of symmetry
Axis of symmetry (C_n), 3
    in ammonia, 4
    and dissymmetric conformations,
        25
    in hydrogen molecule, 4
    in molecules with conical symme-
        try, 6

in molecules with cylindrical symmetry, 5
in molecules with hexagonal symmetry, 10
in molecules with tetrahedral
symmetry, 11, 12
in molecules with trigonal symmetry, 9
in water, 4
α-Azidopropionic acid dimethylamide, asymmetric destruction,
139
Azobenzene, stereoisomers, 84

Baeyer strain
see Angle strain
Baeyer-Villiger oxidation, stereochemistry, 145
Banana bonds
see Bent bonds
Barrier classification of stereoisomers, 51
Barrier to rotation
see Torsional energy barrier
Beckmann rearrangement, stereochemistry, 148
Bending force constant, 35
Bent bonds, 16, 19
in acetylene, 46
in cyclopropane, 19, 20
in ethylene, 20, 21
Benzaldoxime, stereoisomers, 84
Benzene, bond angles, 10
bonding, 23
hexagonal symmetry, 10, 32
molecular models, 44–45
Bicyclo[1.1.0]butane, stereoisomers,
101
Bicyclo[12.12.1]heptacosan-2-one,
stereoisomers, 102
Bicyclo[2.2.0]hexane, stereoisomers,
101
Bicyclo[2.2.2]octane, point group,
47
Bicyclo[3.3.0]octane, stereoisomers,
101
Bicyclo[4.4.1]undecane, bridgehead double bond, 102

Bicyclo[10.1.0]undecane, stereoisomers, 102
1,1'-Binaphthyl, optically active, 78
Biopolymers, helical, asymmetry, 26
optical activity, 106–110
Biot's law, 57
Biphenyls, asymmetric, 26
absolute configuration, 147, 148,
158–160
atropisomerism and racemization,
78–79, 115
dissymmetric but not asymmetric
(C_2 symmetry), 27
dissymmetric, with dihedral symmetry (D_2), 29
as inherently dissymmetric chromophores, 65, 66, 158–160
mutarotation, 163
stereochemistry of substitution at
blocking positions, 145
1,8-Bisdehydro[14]annulene, bonds,
and symmetry, 48
Boat conformation of cyclohexane,
76
π-Bond, 17, 18
breaking in torsion around double
bonds, 37
σ-Bond, 17, 18
τ-Bond
see Bent bond
Bond Angle, in linear molecules, 7
in acetone, 48
in acetyl chloride, 10, 43
in acyclic hydrocarbons, 12, 17
in benzene, 10
in t-butyl t-amyl ketone, 48
in coronene, 9
in cyclobutanone, 48
in cycloheptanone, 48
in cyclohexanone, 48
in cyclopentanone, 48
in cyclopropane, 19, 20
in ethylene, 9
in formaldehyde, 9
in methyl fluoride, 12
in methylene fluoride, 12
in methyl t-butyl ketone, 48
in molecular models, 42–43

in molecules with hexagonal symmetry, 10
in molecules with nonequivalent ligands, 8, 9
in molecules with tetrahedral symmetry, 11, 12, 16
in molecules with trigonal symmetry, 8
in phosgene, 10
and *s*- or *p*-character, 15
Bond angle bending, effect on potential energy, 35
force constant, 35
Bonding geometry in carbon compounds, 5–12
and molecular models, 42–46
Bonding MO, hydrogen molecule, 3
localized, 13
Bonding orbitals in carbon compounds, 13–23
Bond length,
in acetylene, 7, 8
in carbon dioxide, 7
in carbon suboxide, 7
in carbonyl sulfide, 7, 8
change in, effect on potential energy, 3, 34
in hydrogen cyanide, 7
in hydrogen molecule, 3
in molecular models, 43
Bond stretching force constant, 34
Bond torsion, 36
about double bonds, 37, 68, 71
about single bonds, 36, 70
in ferrocene, 47, 71
in molecular models, 43
Bredt rule, 101
Bridgehead olefins, strain, 101, 102
Bromocyclohexane, conformers, 78
Bromocyclopropane, symmetry, 4, 30
1,3-Butadiene, conformers, 75
Butane, conformations, 38
conformers, 70
2-Butanol, absolute configuration, 95, 162
2-Butene, torsion about double bond, 38

cis and *trans,* stability, 38, 67
diastereomers, 67
by dehydration of 2-butanol, 130
geometric isomers, 71
by semihydrogenation of 2-butyne, 128
Buttressing effect, 115
t-Butyl *t*-amyl ketone, bond angle, 48
t-Butylcyclohexane, conformers, 77
sec-Butylmalonic acid, asymmetric decarboxylation, 139, 148, 165
2-Butyne, stereoselective semihydrogenation, 128

C_1 symmetry
see Asymmetry
C_{1h} symmetry, 47
C_{1v} symmetry, 47
C_2 symmetry, 25
C_{2h} symmetry, 30
C_{2v} symmetry, 30
C_3 symmetry in tri-o-thymotide, 26, 29
C_{3v} symmetry, 30
C_{xv} symmetry
see Conical symmetry
Carbanions, geometry, 7
Carbon dioxide, cylindrical symmetry, 5, 7
bond length, 7
linearity, 7
Carbonium ions, geometry, 7, 8
Carbon monoxide, conical symmetry, 6
Carbon suboxide, bond length, 7
cylindrical symmetry, 7, 32
Carbon tetrachloride, tetrahedral symmetry, 11
Carbonyl sulfide, linearity and bond length, 7, 8
conical symmetry, 7, 8
Catenanes, 110, 111
stereoisomers, 112
CD
see Circular dichroism
Cellulose, 105, 106
Center of symmetry (i), 31, 47

Cerebronic acid, configuration, 155
Chair form of cyclohexane
 see Cyclohexane
p-Character of hybrid AO, 15
 effect on bond angle, 15
 and hybridization index, 16
s-Character of hybrid AO, 14, 15
 effect on bond angle, 15
 effect on J_{CH}, 16
 and polarization of electrons, 15
Chirality, 52
 and optical rotatory power, 155–160
Chloroacetylene, conical symmetry, 30
Chloroform, C_{3v} symmetry, 30
1-Chloropropene, torsion in, 38
Chloromethane, C_{3v} conformation, 30
Chromophores, optically active, 63–66
 asymmetrically or dissymmetrically perturbed, 65
 inherently dissymmetric, 65–66
2-Chloro-3-fluorobutane, stereoisomers, 131
Chloramphenicol, stereospecificity of antibiotic activity, 137
C_i symmetry, 31
Circular birefringence, 56, 57
Circular dichroism (CD), 56, 61–62, 66
 in configurational correlations, 155–160
 maxima, positive and negative, 63, 64
Circularly polarized light, 55–56, 62
 in absolute asymmetric synthesis, 139
Cis-conformations, 38
 and geometric isomerism, 71
Cis-trans isomers, 71
 see Geometric isomers
Citric acid, asymmetric degradation, 137–138
C_n symmetry, 23, 32
 and enantiomerism, 51

C_{nh} symmetry, 31, 33
C_{nv} symmetry, 30, 33
Configuration, 82
 absolute
  see Absolute configuration
 corresponding, 96
 geometric isomers, 81–84
 isomers resulting from asymmetric atoms, 86–102
 relative
  see Configurational correlation
Configurational correlation, by chemical methods, 143–145
 by asymmetric synthesis, 145–148
 by comparisons of optical rotations, 154–160
 by the method of phase relationships, 149–154
 by X-ray analysis, 149
Conformation, 24
 absolute, 155
 anti and *gauche,* 37–38
 cis and *trans* in olefins, 38
 dissymmetric, 25
  point groups, 25, 33
 nondissymmetric, 27
  point groups, 25, 33
 and structural isomerism, 50
 and torsional isomerism, 70–71
Conformers, 70
 barrier height, 37, 71
 of cyclohexane, 76–78, 97, 98
 of decalins and perhydrophenanthrenes, 97–100
 gauche and *anti,* 70
 s-*cis* and s-*trans,* 75
Conformational Isomer
 see Conformer
Configurational notation, 94–96
Conglomerate, 70, 150
Conical helix, 26, 28
 point group, 26, 28
Conical Symmetry, 5
 of σ-bonds, 17
 in carbon monoxide, 6
 in carbonyl sulfide, 7
 and coordination number one, 6
 and coordination number two, 6

184

in cyanide ion, 6
of hybrid orbitals, 15
in hydrogen chloride, 5, 7
in hydrogen cyanide, 7
as point group C_{zv}, 30, 47
Coordination number of carbon, 6
one, and conical symmetry, 6
two, in triatomic molecules, 6
and hybrid orbitals, 17, 21
and equivalence or nonequivalence of ligand atoms, 7
and linearity or nonlinearity of
molecular array, 7
and conical symmetry, 7
and cylindrical symmetry, 7
three, and planarity or nonplanarity of molecular array, 7
and hybrid orbitals, 17, 20
and equivalence or nonequivalence of ligand atoms, 7, 8,
13
and bond angles, 7, 8
and trigonal symmetry, 7, 8
four, and equivalence or nonequivalence of ligand atoms,
11
and tetrahedral symmetry, 11,
12
and bond angles, 12
and hybrid orbitals, 17–19
Coronene, bond angles, 10
hexagonal symmetry, 10
C_s-symmetry, 30
Cotton effect, 59, 63–66
in configurational correlations,
155–160
Constitution, 50
J_{CH} Coupling constant and s-character, 16
and bond angles, 19
Cubane, O_h symmetry, 49
spin coupling constant (J_{CH}), 49
Cubic symmetry, as point group O_h,
33, 49
Cumulenes, bonding, 22
cis and trans isomerism, 85
Curtius rearrangement, stereochemistry, 145

Cyanide ion, conical symmetry, 6
Cycloalkanes, acid strength, 47
Cyclobutane, D_{4h} and D_{2d} conformations, 47
angle strain, 47
spin coupling constant (J_{CH}), 49
substituted, stereoisomers, 117
Cyclobutanone, bond angle, 48
Cyclodecane, spin coupling constant
(J_{CH}), 49
Cyclodecene, racemization of trans-
isomer, 86
Cycloheptanone, bond angle, 48
Cyclohexane, spin coupling constant
(J_{CH}), 49
chair (rigid) form, D_{3d} symmetry,
32, 76
molecular models, 44–45
conformers, 76
interconversion, 76, 77
monosubstituted, 77, 78, 166
disubstituted, stereoisomers, 97,
98, 115
flexible form, 77
twist form, 76, 77
Cyclohexanone, bond angle, 48
Cycloöctene, cis and trans isomers,
85
enantiomers of trans isomer, 86,
87
Cyclopentane, C_s (envelope) conformation, 30
spin coupling constant (J_{CH}), 49
Cyclopentanone, bond angle, 48
Cyclopropane, bent bonds, 19, 20
angle strain, 35
D_{3h} symmetry, 32
hybrid orbitals, 19
spin coupling constant (J_{CH}), 49
Cyclopropane-1,2-dicarboxylic acid,
configuration, 142
Cysteine, configuration, 96
Cylindrical axis (C_z), 5
and conical symmetry, 5
and cylindrical symmetry, 5
and hybrid orbitals, 15
and p-orbitals, 13
and spherical symmetry, 6

Cylindrical helix, 26, 28
  absolute configuration, 52, 54, 56, 62, 94
  in biopolymers, 26
  enantiomers and helicity, 52
  in hexahelicene, 26
  palindromic and non-palindromic, 26
  point groups, 26, 28
  in polypeptides (α-helix), 106–108
  in representation of circularly polarized light, 56, 57, 62
  in teflon, 106
Cylindrical symmetry, 5
  in acetylene, 7
  of σ-bonds, 17
  in carbon dioxide, 5, 7
  in carbon suboxide, 7
  and coordination number two, 7
  in hydrogen molecule, 5
  as point group D_{zh}, 32, 47
  of p-orbitals, 13
  of triple bond, 21

D_2 symmetry, in twisted biphenyls, 29
D_{2d} symmetry, 32
D_{2h} symmetry, 32
D_3 symmetry, in skewed ethane, 26
D_{3d} symmetry, 32
D_{3h} symmetry
  see Trigonal symmetry
D_{6h} symmetry
  see Hexagonal symmetry
D_{zh} symmetry
  see Cylindrical symmetry
D-configuration of α-amino and α-hydroxy acids, 96, 97
Decalin, stereoisomers, 98, 99
Degenerate interconversion, 74
  in 3,4-bromotropylidene, 74
  in chair cyclohexane, 76
  in 1,1-difluorocyclohexane, 77, 97
  in disubstituted cyclohexanes, 97
  in perhydroanthracene, 171
  in trans-thianthrene 5, 10-dioxides, 170
Dehydrocamphor, optical activity, 165

Dextro- or d-Isomer, 60
Diamond, coordination number of carbon in, 11
Diastereomers (Diastereoisomers), 51
  configuration, 82, 149
  dissymmetry and optical activity, 68
  distinction between, 53–54, 67
  interconversion, 70
  physical properties, 67
  rates of reaction, 68, 122, 123, 128, 140
  separation, 119
Diastereomeric faces of a carbonyl group, 131, 134
Diastereomeric nuclei (atoms) and groups, 72
  in benzyl compounds, 113
  in diethyl acetal, 94
  in 1,1-difluorocyclohexane, 75
  in 1,1-difluoro-1,2-dibromo-2,2-dichloroethane, 73
  in N,N-dimethylacetamide, 73, 74
  in malic acid, 141
  in methyl compounds, 117
  and molecular dissymmetry, 94
  in propene, 72
  in tactic vinyl polymers, 103–104
Diastereomeric phase relationships, 152–153
Diastereomeric protons (hydrogens)
  see Diastereomeric nuclei
Diastereomeric transition states, 122–140, 148
1,2-Dibromoethane, conformations, 38
2,3-Dibromopentane, stereoisomers, 140
2,3-Dichlorobutane, stereoisomers, 131
1,1-Dichloroethene, C_{2v} symmetry, 30
Trans-1,2-Dichloroethene, C_{2h} symmetry, 32
1,1-Difluoro-1,2-dibromo-2,2-

dichloroethane, conformers, 73
1,1-Difluorocyclohexane, degenerate
    interconversion, 77, 97
1,2-Dihaloethenes, cis and trans,
    stability, 38
    and configuration, 141
Dihedral angle, 4
    change in, effect on potential
        energy, 35
Dihedral symmetry, 26
N,N-Dimethylacetamide, diaster-
    eomeric protons, 75
2,2-Dimethylbiphenyl, race-
    mization, 78
6,6'-Dimethyl-2,2'-biphenyldia-
    mine, configuration, 145
1,4-Dimethylcyclohexane, cis and
    trans isomers, 71
Dimethyldibenzsuberone, chirality
    and ORD, 160
6,6'-Dimethyl-2,2'-diiodobiphenyl,
    configuration, 145
1,2-Dichloroethane, conformations,
    38
Dissymmetric catalysis
    see Asymmetric catalysis
Dissymmetric conformations, 25
    and axes of rotation, 25
    with dihedral symmetry, 26
    in macromolecules, 106–110
    and σ planes, 25
    point groups, 25, 33
Dissymmetrically perturbed symmet-
    ric chromophores, 65
    in configurational correlations,
        155–160
Dissymmetry, 25
    and enantiomerism, 51–54
    manifestation in optical activity,
        61–62
    in topological isomers, 111
Disyndiotactic polymers, 116
dl-Pair:
    see Racemic modification
D_n symmetry, 23, 32
    and enantiomerism, 51
D_{nh} symmetry, 32, 33
DNA, 107, 109

Double bond, 20, 21
    linear deformation, effect on po-
        tential energy, 34
    torsion about, 37
Dreiding models, 44–45
Drude equation, 59, 60

Eclipsed conformation, in ethane,
    24, 25
    D_{3h} symmetry, 32
    transition state in torsion
        about C—C bond, 36
    in ferrocene, 47
    in 1,1,1-trichloroethane, C_{3v}
        symmetry, 30
Electron configuration in carbon,
    13
Electron probability contours, in
    hydrogen molecule, 2
    in hybrid orbitals, 14, 15
    in p-orbitals, 13, 14
Elliptically polarized light, 62
Enantiomers, 51
    configuration, 82
    dissymmetry, 51
    interconversion (racemization),
        69
    optical activity, 53–66, 154–160
    principle underlying distinction
        and separation, 52–54, 119
    rates of reaction, 68, 123–140
    see also Configurational correla-
        tion, Absolute configuration,
        Geometric enantiomerism
Enantiomeric faces of a carbonyl
    group, 129
Enantiomeric nuclei (atoms), 73
    in benzyl compounds, 113
    in 1,1-difluoro-1,2-dibromo-2,2-
        dichloroethane, 73
    relation to meso carbon atom, 127
Enantiomeric protons
    see Enantiomeric nuclei
Enantiomeric purity, 61
Enantiomeric transition states, 126,
    127, 133
Enantiomeric types, in ORD and
    CD, 155

Enantiomorphous crystals, 52, 53
Energy barrier
   see Torsional energy barrier
Envelope form of cyclopentane, 30
Enzymatic processes, stereoselectiv-
   ity, 129, 130
   stereospecificity, 137, 141
Ephedrine, stereoisomers, 90
   absolute configuration, 94
   notation, 96
Epimer, 91
Epimerization, 70
Equatorial bonds in cyclohexane, 76,
   77
Equilibrium conformation, 37, 41
   in torsional isomers, 70, 71
Erythro-diisotactic polymers, 116
Erythro isomer, 96
Erythrose, absolute configuration,
   144
Ethane, conformations, 24, 25
   symmetry, 32
   torsional energy barrier, 36, 37
Ethanol-1-*d,* asymmetric synthesis,
   129
Ethyl-*n*-propyl-*n*-butyl-*n*-hexyl-
   methane, apparent optical inactivity, 61, 81
Ethylcyclohexane, 77
Ethylene, bond angles, 9
   acid strength, 47
   bent bonds, 20, 21
   $\mathbf{D}_{2h}$ symmetry, 32
   spin coupling constant ($\mathbf{J}_{CH}$), 48
Excited states, geometry, 41
Extrema of ORD curve, 60

Ferrocene, symmetry and conformations, 47
   optically active, 112
   torsional barrier, 47
   torsional isomerism, 71
Fischer convention (projection
   formula), 88
Flexible form of cyclohexane, 76, 77
Fluxional structure, 74
Formaldehyde, bond angles, 9
   bonding, 23

$\mathbf{C}_{2v}$ symmetry, 30
   geometry in excited state, 41
Framework Molecular Orbital
   (Brumlik) models, 44–45
Fumarate, fumarase catalyzed
   hydration, 141

Gauche-conformations, 38
   and conformational isomerism, 70
Geometric enantiomerism, 85
   and absolute configuration, 146,
   148
Geometric isomers, 71
   cis and *trans,* 71, 82
   relative stability, 38, 82–85
   isomer numbers, 81, 83
   see also Geometric enantiomers
   α- and β-Glucose, asymmetric transformation, 122
   absolute configuration, 145
Glyceraldehyde, absolute configuration, 96, 145, 166
Graphite, coordination of carbon in,
   8
Gutta-percha, stereochemistry, 105

Handedness
   see Chirality
Helix, conical
   see Conical helix
   cylindrical *see* Cylindrical helix
Hepta-2,5-dien-4-ol, stereoisomers,
   97
Heptaric acid, stereoisomers, 91, 92
   analogy with tactic polymers,
   104
Hexahydromandelic acid, configuration, 155
Hexagonal symmetry, in benzene, 10
   and bond angles, 10
   in coronene, 10
   as point group $\mathbf{D}_{6h}$, 32
Hexahelicene, $\mathbf{C}_2$ symmetry, 26
   inherently dissymmetric chromophore, 66
   resolution of racemic form, 121
Hexamethyltricyclo[3.1.0.0^{2,4}]
   hexane, 118

Hofmann rearrangement, stereochemistry, 145
Homohydratropic acid, configuration, 145
3,4-Homotropylidene, degenerate
 interconversion, 74
Hybrid orbitals, 14
 and bent bonds, 19
 conical symmetry, 15
 and coordination numbers two,
  three, and four, 17–21
 electron probability contour, 14,
  15
 nodal surface, 14
 p-character, 15
 s-character, 14, 15
Hybridization, 14, 16
 index, 16
 and molecular models, 43
 parameter
 see Mixing coefficient
 relation to bond angles, 16–21
Hydratropic acid, configuration, 145
Hydrogen chloride, conical symmetry, 5, 30
Hydrogen cyanide, linearity, and
 bond lengths, 7
 conical symmetry, 7
Hydrogen molecule, bond length, 3
 axes of rotation, 4
 bonding MO, 3
 cylindrical symmetry, 4
 electron probability contours, 2
 planes of symmetry, 4
α-Hydroxy acids, configuration,
 96, 145, 155, 161

Identity reaction
 see Degenerate Interconversion
Improper axis
 see Rotation-reflection axis
Inherently dissymmetric chromophores, 65–66
 in configurational correlations,
  155–160
Inositol, stereoisomers, 115
Internuclear angle, 19
 in molecular models, 42

Interorbital angle, 19
 in cyclopropane, 20
Isoleucine, absolute configuration,
 143
Isomers, structural, classification,
 50–54
 constitutional, 50
Isomorphism, 151–154
Isoprene polymers, stereochemistry,
 105
Isopropylcyclohexane, 77
Isorotation rules, 154
Isotactic polymers, 104, 106
Isotope dilution technique for the
 estimation of optical purity, 167

Ketones, relation of carbonyl absorption and bond angle, 48
 absolute configuration, 156–160,
  165
 asymmetric reduction, 129, 131–
  134, 167
Kinetic resolution, 135–139, 167
 and configurational correlation,
  145–148

L-configuration of α-amino and α-
 hydroxy acids, 96, 97
Lactic acid, absolute configuration,
 145, 155
Levo- or *l*-Isomer, 60
Ligand atoms, 6
Linear molecules, and coordination
 number, 6
 and equivalence or nonequivalence of ligands in dicoördi-
  nate carbon, 7
Linoleic acid, isomers, 82
Linolenic acid, isomers, 82
Lone pairs of electrons
 see Nonbonding electrons

Macromolecules, stereochemistry,
 102–110
Malic acid, asymmetric synthesis,
 141
 asymmetric oxidation, 137
Mandelic acid, configuration, 161

Manual separation of enantiomorphous forms, 52, 61, 119
Meso carbon atom, 127, 129, 131
in the citric acid degradation, 137
in the stearic acid dehydrogenation, 173
Meso-Isomer, 81
in compounds with asymmetric atoms, 88, 90–92, 97
in terphenyls, 81
Methane, tetrahedral symmetry, 11, 12
spin coupling constant ($\mathbf{J}_{\mathrm{CH}}$), 48
Methyl acetylene, spin coupling constant ($\mathbf{J}_{\mathrm{CH}}$), 49
Methyl *t*-butyl ketone, bond angle, 48
asymmetric reduction, 131
Methyl cation, trigonal symmetry, 8, 32
Methylcyclohexane, conformers, 77
Methylene chloride, $\mathbf{C}_{2v}$ symmetry, 30
Methyl fluoride, bond angles, 12
N-Methylformamide, conformers, 75
Methyl formate, conformers, 75
4-Methyl-2-hexene, stereoisomers, 97
Methyl nitrite, conformers, 75
3-Methylpentanoic acid, asymmetric synthesis, 140
Mirror axis:
see Rotation-reflection axis
Mirror image, 24
habit, 52
Mirror symmetry
see Reflection symmetry
Mixing coefficient, 14
Models, molecular, 1, 42–46
Molecular deformations and strain energies, 33–41
as reflected by molecular models, 43
types, 34
Molecular ellipticity, 62
Molecular models, 1, 42–46
Molecular rotation, 58
see also Optical rotation
Morphine, configuration, 117

stereospecificity of analgesic activity, 137
Mutarotation, 70, 163–164
Mycomycin, stereoisomers, 116

Naphthalene, $\mathbf{D}_{2h}$ symmetry, 32
Nemotinic acid, stereoisomers, 116
Neopentane, tetrahedral symmetry, 11
Newman projection, 24, 26–29, 31, 32
Nitromethane, torsional barrier, 36
Nitrosyl chloride, plane of symmetry, 4
symmetry ($\mathbf{C}_s$), 30
Nodal surface, in *p*-orbital, 13, 14
in hybrid orbitals, 14, 15
Nonbonded interactions, 38
in molecular models, 43
potential functions expressing, 38–40
Nonbonding electrons, 6
in formaldehyde, 23
role in coordination sphere of carbon, 7
Nondissymmetric conformations, 27
point groups, 25, 33
*Nor*bornane, point group, 47
*Nor*camphor, stereoisomers, 101, 102
Nucleic acids, optically active, 106, 107, 109

$\mathbf{O}_h$ symmetry, 33, 49
Octant rule, 157, 159, 165
Oleic acid, isomers, 82, 145
Optically active chromophores, 63–66
in configurational correlations, 155–160
Optical activation, 120
as related to configurational correlation, 145
Optical activity (Optical rotatory power), 54–66, 154–160
see also Optical rotation
Optical antipode
see Enantiomer

Optical isomers, 111, 113
Optically active polymers, 106–110
Optically active transitions, 63
Optical purity, 61
  by isotope dilution, 167
Optical resolution, 120–121
Optical rotation, 57
  conditions for observation, 60–61
  in configurational correlation,
    154–160
  dependence on wavelength, 58–60
  in macromolecules, 109
  magnitude and sign, dependence
    on conditions of measure-
    ment, 58
  dependence on structure, 63–66
  as manifestation of molecular dis-
    symmetry, 61–62
  vicinal effect, 154
Optical rotatory dispersion (ORD),
  58
  in configurational correlations,
    155–160
  overlapping of curves, 64
  in relation to Cotton effect, 59
Optical stability, 61
p-Orbitals, 13
  cylindrical symmetry, 13
  electron probability contour, 13,
    14
  nodal surface, 13
s-Orbitals, 13
  electron density, 14
  spherical symmetry, 13
ORD
  see Optical rotatory dispersion
Overcrowding, in racemization of
  biphenyls, 77
Overlap of atomic orbitals, 13
  to form σ- and π-bonds, 17, 18

Palindromic helix
  see Cylindrical helix
Paracyclophanes, atropisomerism,
  81
Parasantonide, configuration and optical rotation, 160
Peak of ORD curve, 60

Penicillium glaucum, asymmetric re-
  struction, 136
Pentaric acid, stereoisomers, 90,
  144
2-Pentene, stereoisomers, 140
Perhydroanthracenes, stereoisomers,
  115
Perhydrophenanthrene,
  stereoisomers, 99, 100
Periodicity, in bond torsion, 36
  and energy barrier, 36
Phase relationships between stereoisomers, 152–154
α-Phenethyl alcohol, configuration,
  145, 162
α-Phenethylamine, configuration,
  145
α-Phenethylketene, configuration,
  145
3-Phenyl-2-butanol, stereoisomers,
  131, 162
Phosgene, bond angles, 9
Pitzer strain
  see Torsional strain
Plain ORD curve, 60
σ-Plane
  see Plane of symmetry
Plane polarized light, 55–56
  rotation, 57
Plane of symmetry (σ), 3
  bisecting angle between enantio-
    meric protons, 73
  and dihedral symmetry, 26, 32
  and dissymmetric conformations,
    25
  identity with S_1, 47
  in molecules with conical sym-
    metry, 5
  in molecules with cylindrical
    symmetry, 5
  in molecules with hexagonal
    symmetry, 10
  in molecules with tetrahedral
    symmetry, 11, 12
  in molecules with trigonal sym-
    metry, 9
  and nondissymmetric conforma-
    tions, 28

Point group, 23–33
  of dissymmetric conformations, 25, 33
  of nondissymmetric conformations, 25, 33
Point of symmetry
  see Center of symmetry
Polarimetry, 60
Polarized light
  see Plane, Circularly, and Elliptically polarized light
Poly-isoprene, 105
Poly-α-olefins
  see Vinyl polymers
Polypeptides, 106
Polysaccharides, 105, 106
Primary structure of macromolecules, 106
Proper axis
  see Axis of symmetry
Propyl chloride, torsion in, 37
  conformations, 38
Propylene oxide, optically active polymerization, 106
Pseudoasymmetric atoms, 91
  in tactic polymers, 104

Quartz, enantiomorphous forms, 52, 53
  dissymmetric structure, 56
Quasi-enantiomers, 152
Quasi-racemate, 152

(R)-Configuration, 95
Racemate, 69, 150
Racemic (dl) modification, 68–69
Racemic mixture
  see Conglomerate
Racemization, 69, 93
Reflection symmetry, 24
  recognition of, by inspection of models, 42
Resolution of racemic forms, 120–121
Resolving agent, 120
Restricted rotation, 37
  as reflected in molecular models, 42–46
Ricinoleic acid, stereoisomers, 115

Rotamer
  see Conformer
Rotation about bonds
  see Bond torsion
Rotation, optical
  see Optical rotation
Rotation-reflection axis (S_n), 24
Rotational barrier
  see Torsional energy barrier
Rotational isomers
  see Conformers, Atropisomers
Rotational strength, 63
Rubber, 105
Rule of shift, 154
Rule of superposition, 154
Rules of isorotation, 154

S-Methylcysteine, configuration, 149
S-Methylcysteine-S-oxide, configuration, 149, 150
S_2 symmetry, 31
S_4 symmetry, 31
s-Cis and s-Trans isomers, 75
(S)-configuration, 95
Screw
  see Conical helix
Secondary structure of macromolecules, 106
Second-order asymmetric transformation, 122, 164
Simple axis
  see Axis of symmetry
Skewed conformation, in ethane, 24, 25
  point group (D_3), 26
  as torsional mode, 37
  in ferrocene, 47
S_n symmetry, 30, 31, 33
Sodium ammonium tartrate, enantiomorphous forms, 52, 53, 61
Solid solution formation, 150, 153
Specific rotation, 58
  see also Optical rotation
Spectropolarimetry, 60
Spherical symmetry, 6
  of s-orbitals, 13
Sphingosine, stereoisomers, 116
Spiranes, stereoisomerism, 86, 117,

165
Spiropentane, hybridization of central carbon, 46
Staggered conformation, in ethane, 24, 25
D_{3d} symmetry, 32
as equilibrium conformation, 37
ferrocene, 47
Starch, 105, 106
Stereoblock polymer, 105
Stereoisomers, 50–118
see also Enantiomers, Diastereomers, Torsional stereoisomers, etc.
definition and classification, 51
Stereoselectivity, 128
in biological and nonbiological processes, 129
Stereospecificity, 137
Steric effects
see Nonbonded interactions
Stilbene, stereoisomers, 84
Strain energies and molecular deformations, 33–41
as reflected by molecular models, 43
Structure, molecular, 1
Structural isomers, classification, 50–54
Stuart-Briegleb models, 44–45
Sugars, configurational correlations, 144
Sulforaphene, stereoisomers, 116
Sulfoxides, 88
absolute configuration, 149, 150
inherently dissymmetric chromophores, 66
optically active, 164
Symmetry arguments, 9, 10, 12
Symmetry axis
see Axis of symmetry
Symmetry classification of stereoisomers, 51
Symmetry, conical
see Conical symmetry
Symmetry, cylindrical
see Cylindrical symmetry
Symmetry elements, 3, 24

Symmetry, hexagonal
see Hexagonal symmetry
Symmetry number, 33
Symmetry plane
see Plane of symmetry
Symmetry, tetrahedral
see Tetrahedral symmetry
Symmetry, trigonal
see Trigonal symmetry
Syndiotactic polymers, 104

Tactic polymerization
see Vinyl polymerization
Tacticity, 105
Tartaric acid, C_2 conformation of the active form, 28
absolute configuration, 143, 144
reason for optical inactivity of meso-form, 89
S_2 conformation of meso-form, 31
stereoisomers, 88–89
T_d symmetry
see Tetrahedral symmetry
Terphenyls, atropisomers, 80, 82
1,1,2,2-Tetrabromoethane, conformations, 38
Tetrabutylmethane, isomers, 90
Tetrachlorocubane, isomers, 113, 117
1,1,2,2-Tetrachloroethane, conformations, 38
Tetrahedral carbon atom, 11
in molecular models, 42
Tetrahedral symmetry, 11
and bond angles, 11
in carbon tetrachloride, 11
and coordination number four, 11
and hybrid orbitals, 17
in methane, 11, 12
in neopentane, 11
as point group T_d, 33
2,2,5,5-Tetramethyl-3-hexene, cis and trans, 38, 84
Thianthrene 5,10-dioxides, stereoisomers, 118
Threo-diisotactic polymers, 116
Threo isomer, 96
Threose, absolute configuration,

144, 166
Toluene, conformations, 48
Topological isomerism, 110–111
Torsional double bond isomers
  see Geometric isomers
Torsional energy barrier, 36
  in acetaldehyde, 36
  and atropisomerism, 78–81
  in ethane, 36
  in nitromethane, 36
  and periodicity, 36
Torsional single bond isomers
  see Conformers
Torsional stereoisomerism, 70–86
Torsional strain, 36
  absence in molecular models, 43
Trans-conformation, 38
  and geometric isomerism, 71
Trefoil, 110, 111
Triatomic molecules, and coordination number, 6
Trigonal symmetry, 8
  and bond angles, 8
  and coordination number three, 7
  in methyl cation, 8
  as point group D_{3h}, 32
Tri-o-thymotide, C_3 symmetry, 26, 29
  enantiomerism and racemization, 80
  optical activation, 121
Triple bond, 21
Tröger's base, 88
  configuration at asymmetric nitrogen, 95

resolution of racemic form, 121
stereoisomers, 101
Trough of ORD curve, 60
Truxillic acid, stereoisomers, 111
Truxinic acid, stereoisomers, 112
Twistane, point group, 47
Twist form of cyclohexane, 76, 77

Vicinal effect in optical rotation, 154
Vinyl chloride, symmetry, 4, 30
Vinyl polymerization, stereochemistry, 102–105
  by *cis*-addition, 104–105, 116
  by *trans*-addition, 103, 116
  tactic, 103
Vinyl polymers, stereoisomers, 102–105
  atactic, 104
  diisotactic, 116
  disyndiotactic, 116
  isotactic, 104
  syndiotactic, 104
V symmetry, 29
V_d symmetry, 31

Water, twofold axis of symmetry, 4
  C_{2v} symmetry, 30
  planes of symmetry, 4
Wolff rearrangement, stereochemistry, 145

X-ray structure and absolute configuration, 142, 149
Xylose, absolute configuration, 144

DISCARD

207954

COALINGA STACKS
207954
547.12 MIS
Introduction to stereochemistry.

DATE DUE

West Hills College Coalinga
Fitch Library
305 Cherry Lane
Coalinga, CA 93210

DISCARD